Chambers, He
The treasuals.

OCT. 12 1978
OCT 3 '80

Y0-AHG-123

M782.253 Treasur
The treasury of Negro spirituals /

THE TR

DATE DUE

(11-22)

SEP 13 1979

APR 0 1 2002

AUG 4 1981
FEB 3 1985

JUN 1 2 2002

JUL 5 1985

MAR 2 5 2006

SEP 2 5 1985

SEP 13 2007

Evanston Public Library
Evanston, Illinois

Each reader is responsible for all books or other materials taken on his card, and for any fines or fees charged for overdues, damages, or loss.

DEMCO, INC. 38-2931

DEMCO

M782.253
Treasur

THE TREASURY OF
NEGRO SPIRITUALS

Edited by
H. A. CHAMBERS

You can play a tune of sorts on the white keys, and you can play a tune of sorts on the black keys, but for harmony you must use both the white and the black. — *AGGREY*

New York
EMERSON BOOKS, INC.

Published 1963 by Emerson Books, Inc.
Library of Congress Catalog Card Number: 63-14218

Second Impression 1968
Third Impression 1970

Copyright Note

All arrangements bearing the Editor's initials, H.A.C., are copyright and must not be reproduced without permission of the copyright owner

---

Acknowledgment

The further permission of Boosey & Hawkes Inc. New York, for the inclusion of "The Lord's Prayer" is acknowledged.

Copyright © 1959 Blandford Press Ltd.,
All rights reserved
MANUFACTURED IN GREAT BRITAIN

CONTENTS

	Page
Foreword by Marian Anderson	9

Traditional Spirituals

A little more faith in Jesus	11
Ain't goin' to study war no more	12
Balm in Gilead	14
By an' by	16
Deep river	19
De Gospel Train	21
Didn't my Lord deliver Daniel?	23
Dry bones	26
Ev'rybody got to die	31
Ev'ry time I feel de Spirit	32
Give me Jesus	36
Go down, Moses	38
He never said a mumbalin' word	39
He's jus' de same today	40
I couldn't hear nobody pray	42
I got a home in-a dat Rock	44
I got a robe	47
I want to be a Christian in my heart	49
I want to be ready	50
Joshua fight de battle ob Jericho	52
Listen to de lam's	55
Little David, play on your harp	58
My Lord, what a morning	60
My soul is a witness for my Lord	62
Nobody knows de trouble I see	65
Oh, wasn't that a wide river?	66
O Peter, go ring-a dem bells	68
Roll, Jordan, roll	70
Sinner, please don't let dis harvest pass	71
Somebody's knocking at your door	75
Standin' in de need of prayer	78
Steal away	80
Swing low, sweet chariot	82
The Lord's Prayer	84
Were you there?	87

Modern Compositions

Be still and listen	89
Ol' man Devil gotta go some	94
Restitution	99
Ride on, King Jesus!	111
Roll away that stone	116
The Glow Within	121
Trouble	124

THE SCRAPER-BOARD ILLUSTRATIONS ARE BY ROBIN ANDERSON

EDITOR'S NOTE

MUSICAL NOTATION is incapable of expressing the various nuances which negro singers employ in singing spirituals, and any attempt to imitate them is to be deprecated. The arrangements in this book have been designed to provide appropriate and attractive accompaniments within the power of an average pianist, without over embellishing the simple folk melodies.

I am grateful to Dr. Marshall Cartledge and to Dr. Will Reed for their interest and suggestions in the compilation of this book.

H. A. C.

FOREWORD

MUSIC mirrors the thinking and feelings of societies. Much that is greatest and richest in a nation or community is preserved through its music. Across barriers of class, race and nationality it can speak from heart to heart.

This is particularly true of the Negro spiritual. These folk songs reflect the warm hearts and firm faith of the Negro peoples. They are songs of aspiration and hope in the face of crisis.

It is my wish that these very gifts of faith and warmth of heart may be nourished afresh for all men, and I accordingly welcome the presentation of this new volume.

Marian Anderson

A little more faith in Jesus

Ain't goin' to study war no more

Balm in Gilead

Deep river

Arranged by H.A.C.

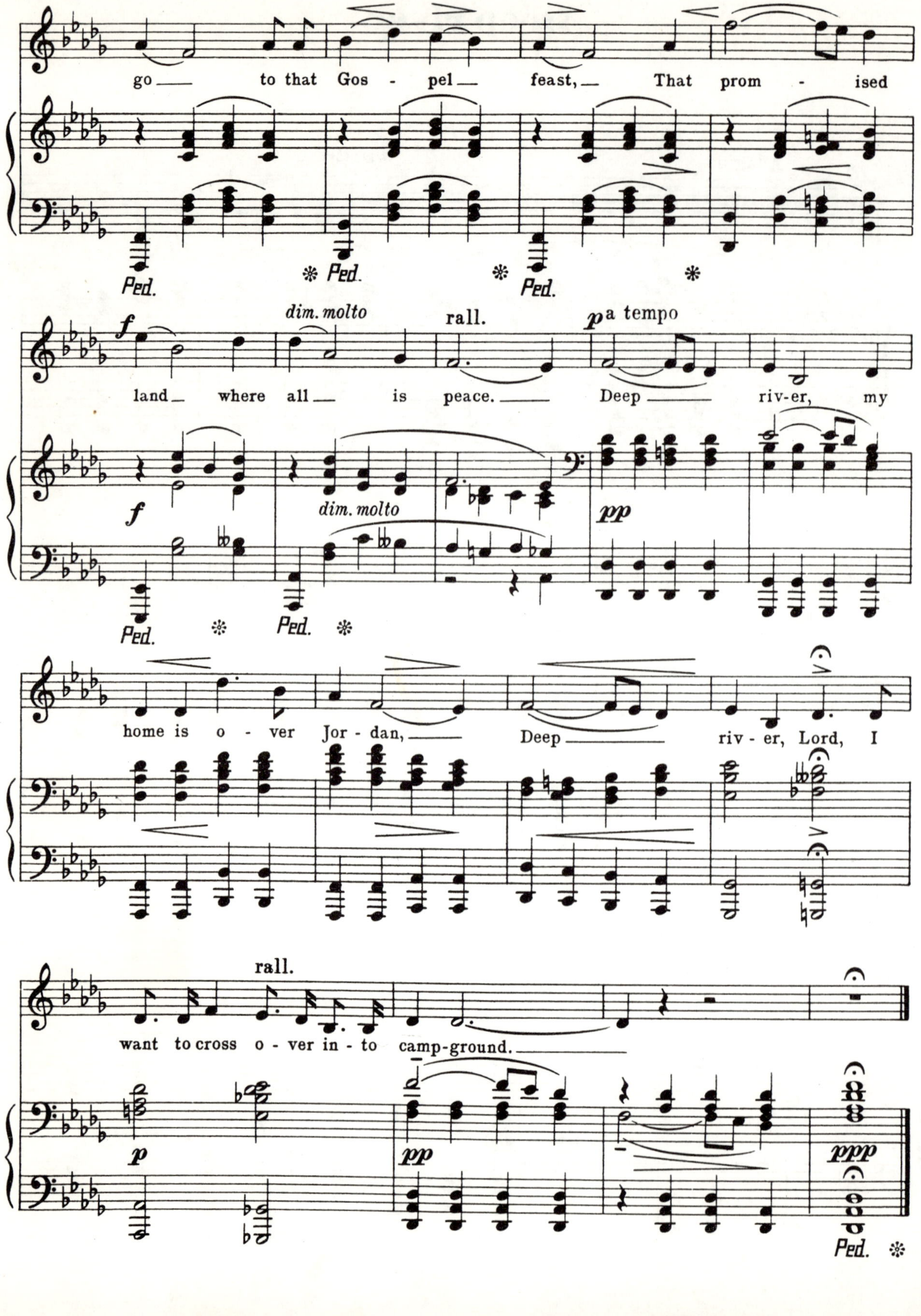
go — to that Gos - pel — feast, — That prom - ised
Ped.
* Ped.
* Ped.
*
dim. molto
rall.
p a tempo
f
land — where all — is peace. — Deep — riv-er, my
f
dim. molto
pp
Ped.
* Ped.
*
home is o - ver Jor - dan, — Deep — riv - er, Lord, I
rall.
want to cross o - ver in - to camp-ground. —
p
pp
ppp
Ped.
*

De Gospel Train

Arranged by H.A.C.

Didn't my Lord deliver Daniel?

Arranged by H.A.C.

Dry bones

Arranged by H.A.C.

Ev'ry time I feel de Spirit

Arranged by H.A.C.

He never said a mumbalin' word

Arranged by H.A.C.

2. They nailed Him to the tree.
3. They pierced Him in the side.
4. The blood came twinkling down.
5. He bowed His head and died.

He's jus' de same today

Arranged by H.A.C.

Moderato

1. When Mo-ses an' his sol-diers from E-gypt's land did flee, His en-e-mies were in be-hind him, An' in front of him de sea, God raised de wa-ters like a wall, An'

2. When Dan-iel, faith-ful to his God, would not bow down to man, An' by God's en-e-my he was hurled In-to de li-on's den, God locked de li-on's jaw, we read, An'

41

I couldn't hear nobody pray

Arranged by H.A.C.

Moderato

And I could-n't hear no-bo-dy pray, And I could-n't hear no-bo-dy pray; O way down yon-der by my-self, And I could-n't hear no-bo-dy pray.

1. In the val-ley,___ On my knees,___ With my bur-den___ And my
2. Hal-le-lu-jah! Trou-bles o-ver!___ In the King-dom___ With my

43

I got a home in-a dat Rock

Arranged by H.A.C.

Rather quickly

cresc.

see? Poor man Laz-'rus, poor as I, Don't you see? Poor man Laz-'rus, poor as I, When he died he foun' a home on high, He had a home in-a dat Rock, Don't you see? Rich man Di-ves lived so well, Don't you see? Rich man Di-ves lived so well, Don't you see? Rich man

Di-ves lived so well, When he died he went to hell, He had no home in-a dat Rock, Don't you see? God gave No-ah de rain-bow sign, Don't you see? God gave No-ah de rain-bow sign, Don't you see? God gave No-ah de rain-bow sign, No mo' wa-ter, but fire next time, Bet-ter get a home in-a dat Rock, Don't you see?

I got a robe

Arranged by **H.A.C.**

Rather quickly

1. I got a robe, you got a robe, All God's chil-lun got a robe; When I get to Hea-b'n gwin' to put on my robe, Gwin' to shout all o-ber God's
2. I got a shoes, you got a shoes, All God's chil-lun got a shoes; When I get to Hea-b'n gwin' to put on my shoes, Gwin' to walk all o-ber God's
3. I got a harp, you got a harp, All God's chil-lun got a harp; When I get to Hea-b'n gwin' to play on my harp, Gwin' to play all o-ber God's

48

Hea - b'n, _____ Hea - b'n, _____ Hea - b'n, _____
Hea - b'n, _____ Hea - b'n, _____ Hea - b'n, _____
Hea - b'n, _____ Hea - b'n, _____ Hea - b'n, _____

Ev-'ry-bo-dy talk-in' 'bout Hea-b'n ain't go-in' there, Hea-b'n, _____
Ev-'ry-bo-dy talk-in' 'bout Hea-b'n ain't go-in' there, Hea-b'n, _____
Ev-'ry-bo-dy talk-in' 'bout Hea-b'n ain't go-in' there, Hea-b'n, _____

Hea - b'n, _____ Gwin' to shout all o - ber God's Hea - b'n. _____
Hea - b'n, _____ Gwin' to walk all o - ber God's Hea - b'n. _____
Hea - b'n, _____ Gwin' to play all o - ber God's Hea - b'n. _____

To Devar Surya Sena

I want to be a Christian in my heart

Arranged by WILL REED

Quiet but not too slow

1. Lord, I want to be a Christ-ian in my heart, in my heart, Lord, I
2. Lord, I want to be more lov-ing in my heart, in my heart, Lord, I
3. O, I don't want to be like Ju-das in my heart, in my heart, O, I
4. Lord, I want to be like Je-sus in my heart, in my heart, Lord, I

CHORUS (*humming*) or PIANO

want to be a Christ-ian in my heart, In my heart, In my
want to be more lov-ing in my heart, In my heart, In my
don't want to be like Ju-das in my heart, In my heart, In my
want to be like Je-sus in my heart, In my heart, In my

(In my heart)

(rit. *last verse*)

heart, Lord, I want to be a Christ-ian in my heart.
heart, Lord, I want to be more lov-ing in my heart.
heart, O, I don't want to be like Ju-das in my heart.
heart, Lord, I want to be like Je-sus in my heart.

(In my heart)

Copyright, 1949, by The Oxford Group, 4, Hay's Mews, London, W.1.

I want to be ready

Arranged by H.A.C.

just like John; {And he declared he'd meet me there,} Walk in Je-ru-sa-lem
{That I'll be there at Judg-ment Day,}
just like John. I want to be rea - dy, I want to be rea - dy,
I want to be rea - dy To walk in Je-ru-sa-lem just like John.

Joshua fight de battle ob Jericho

Arrrnged by H.A.C.

Vigorously

Josh-ua fight de bat-tle ob Je-ri-cho, Je-ri-cho, Je-ri-cho, Josh-ua fight de bat-tle ob Je-ri-cho, An' de walls come tum-blin' down.

You may talk a-bout yo' king ob Gid-e-on, You may talk a-bout yo' man ob

Saul; Dere's none like good ole Josh-u-a At de bat-tle ob Je-ri-cho.

Up to de walls ob Je-ri-cho He marched with spear in han'. "Go blow dem rams' horns," Josh-ua cried, "'Cos de bat-tle am in my han'."

Den de lam' ram sheep horns 'gin to blow, Trumpets be-gin to soun',

*If desired the first section between the double bars may be used as a refrain at these points.

54

Josh-ua com-mand-ed de chil-dren to shout, An' de walls come tum-blin' down. Josh-ua fight de bat-tle ob Je-ri-cho, Je-ri-cho, Je-ri-cho, Josh-ua fight de bat-tle ob Je-ri-cho, An' de walls come tum-blin' down.

Listen to de lam's

don't be a-fraid, Wan-ta go to heab'n when I die; De Lord for you in de groun' was laid,— Wan-ta go to heab'n when I die. O mind out, brud-der, how ye walk de cross, Wan-ta go to heab'n when I die. Yo' foot might slip an' yo' soul get a los',—

57

Wan - ta go to heab'n when I die. Lis - ten to de lam's ___ all a-cry-in', ___ Lis - ten to de lam's ___ all a - cry - in', Lis - ten to de lam's ___ all a - cry - in', I wan-ta go to heab'n when I die.

Little David, play on your harp

Arranged by H.A.C.

lu! Lit-tle Da-vid, play on your harp, Hal - le - lu! Josh-ua was de son of Nun, He nev-er would quit till his work was done. Lit-tle Da-vid, play on your harp, Hal - le - lu, hal - le - lu! Lit-tle Da-vid, play on your harp, Hal - le - lu!

My Lord, what a morning

Arranged by H.A.C.

Moderato

My Lord, what a morn-ing, My Lord, what a morn-ing, My Lord, what a morn-ing When de stars be-gin to fall.

1. You'll hear de trum-pet sound,
3. You'll hear de Christ-ians shout,

To wake de na-tions un-der ground, Look-in' to my God's right hand, When de

cresc.
p
stars be-gin to fall. My Lord, what a morn-ing, My Lord, what a
p
cresc.
Ped. * Ped. *
mf
last v. rall.
p
v. 3 Fine
morn-ing, My Lord, what a morn-ing When de stars be-gin to fall.
mf
Ped. * Ped. * Ped. * Ped. * Ped. * Ped. * Ped. *
v. 1
mf
fall. 2. You'll hear de sin-ner moan, To wake de na-tions un-der
mf
cresc.
dim.
D.S. al Fine
p
ground, Look-in' to my God's right hand When de stars be-gin to fall.
cresc.
dim.
p

My Soul is a witness for my Lord

Arranged by H.A.C.

Rather quick

My Soul is a wit-ness for my Lord, my Soul is a wit-ness for my Lord. My for my Lord.

1. You read in de Bi-ble, an' you un-der-stan', Me-thu-se-lah was de old-es' man; He lived nine hun-dred an' six-ty nine,— He died an' went to Hea-ven, Lord,
2. You read in de Bi-ble, an' you un-der-stan', Sam-son was de strong-es' man; Sam-son went out at a one time,— An' he killed a-bout a thou-sand ob de

in a due time. O Me - thuse-lah was a wit - ness_ for my Lord, Me -
Phil - is - tine. O Sam-son was a wit - ness_ for my Lord, O
thuse-lah was a wit - ness for my Lord.
Sam-son was a wit - ness for my Lord.
3. Now Dan-iel was_ a He-brew chile, He
went to pray to his God a - while; De king at once for Dan-iel did sen',_ An' he
put him right down in de li - on's den. God sent his An-gels de
cresc.
D. S.
Ped.

li - ons for to keep, An' Dan-iel laid down an' went to sleep. Now Dan-iel was a wit - ness for my Lord, Now Dan-iel was a wit - ness for my Lord. My Soul is a wit - ness for my Lord, my Soul is a wit-ness for my Lord.

Nobody knows de trouble I see

Arranged by H.A.C.

66

Nobody knows de trouble I see, Nobody knows but Jesus;

Nobody knows de trouble I see, Glory, Halle-lujah!

Oh, wasn't that a wide river?

Arranged by H.A.C.

Brightly

Oh, was-n't that a wide river, river of Jordan, Lord? Wide river, There's

67

O Peter, go ring-a dem bells

Arranged by H.A.C.

day, I heard from heav-en to - day; I thank God, and I thank you too; I heard from heav'n to - day. O Pe-ter, go ring-a dem bells, Pe-ter, go ring-a dem bells, Pe-ter, go ring-a dem bells, I heard from heav'n to - day.

Roll, Jordan, roll

Arranged by H.A.C.

Roll, Jor-dan, roll, roll, Jor-dan, roll, I want to go to Heav-en when I die To hear Jor-dan roll. O

{ broth-ers / preach-ers / sin-ners } you ought to ha' been there, Yes, my Lord, A sit-tin' in the King-dom To hear Jor-dan roll. Roll, Jor-dan,

Sinner, please don't let dis harvest pass

Arranged by H.A.C.

pass,_____ Sin-ner, please don't let dis har-vest pass, An' die, an' lose your soul at last._____

Sin-ner, O__ see dat cru-el tree,_____ Sin-ner, O__ see dat cru-el tree,_____ Sin-ner, O__ see dat cru-el tree Where Christ has died for you and me.

My God is a might-y man of war, My God is a might-y man of war, My God is a might-y man of war, Sin-ner, please don't let dis har-vest pass.

mp
cresc.
Sin-ner, please don't let dis har-vest pass. Sin-ner,
p
please don't let dis har-vest pass, Sin-ner,
please don't let dis har - vest pass, And
f
mf
dim.
rall.
p
die, and lose your soul at last.
pp
pp
Ped.

Somebody's knocking at your door

Arranged by H.A.C.

Knocks like— Je-sus, Some-bo-dy's knock-in' at your door.

Can't you— hear him? Some-bo-dy's knock-in' at your door.

O———— sin-ner, why don't you an-swer? Some-bo-dy's knock-in' at your door.———— Je-sus— calls you, Some-bo-dy's knock-in' at your door._____ Can't you__ trust him?

Some-bo-dy's knock-in' at your door._____ O__

sin-ner, why don't you an-swer? Some-bo-dy's knock-in' at your

door._____

dim.

p

Standin' in de need of prayer

Arranged by H.A.C.

Moderato

It's me, it's me, O Lord, Stand-in' in de need of prayer, It's me, it's me, O Lord, Stand-in' in de need of prayer.

1. Not my bro-ther, nor my sis-ter,
2. Not the preach-er, nor the dea-con,

but it's me, O Lord,

Stand-in' in de need of prayer, {Not my bro-ther, nor my sis-ter, / Not the preach-er, nor the dea-con,} but it's me, O Lord, Stand-in' in de need of prayer. It's me, it's me, O Lord, Stand-in' in de need of prayer, It's

cresc. *f* *(last v. rall.)* D.S.

me, it's me, O Lord, Stand-in' in de need of prayer.

Steal away

Arranged by H.A.C.

Steal a-way, steal a-way, steal a-way to Je-sus! Steal a-way, steal a-way home, I ain't got long to stay here.

1. My Lord calls me, He calls me by the thun-der;
2. My Lord calls me, He calls me by the light-ning;

The

p
trum-pet sounds with-in-a my soul: I ain't got long to stay here.
p
Steal a-way, steal a-way, steal a-way to Je-sus! Steal a-way,
mf
pp
mf
rall.
D.S.
after v. 2
steal a-way home, I ain't got long to stay here.
pp
morendo
ppp
Ped.
Ped.
Ped.

Swing low, sweet chariot

Arranged by H.A.C.

what did I see,— Com-in' for to car-ry me home? A band of an-gels *cresc. molto* com-in' af-ter me,— Com-in' for to car-ry me home. Swing low, sweet cha - ri - ot,— Com-in' for to car-ry me home; Swing low sweet cha - ri - ot,— Com-in' for to car-ry me home.

To Marian Anderson

The Lord's Prayer

Tune taken down by OLIVE PATTISON
Arranged by WILL REED

Quiet, but not too slow

Our Father, which art in Heaven, Hallow-èd a-be Thy name; Thy Kingdom come, Thy will be done, Hallow-èd a-be Thy name; On the earth as it is in Heaven, Hallow-èd a-be Thy name; Give us this day our daily bread, Hallow-èd a-be Thy name; And forgive us all our trespasses,

Melody and words reprinted by permission of Boosey & Hawkes Ltd.
Arrangement copyright, 1953, by Will Reed

Hal-low-èd a - be Thy name; As we for-give those who tres-pass a-gainst us,

poco f

Hal-low-èd a - be Thy name; And lead us not to the De-vil to be tempt-ed,

p

Hal-low-èd a - be Thy name; But de - liv - er us from all that is e - vil,

ten. ten. ten. ten.

f

Hal-low-èd a - be Thy name; For Thine is the King-dom, the pow-er and the glo-ry,

Hal-low-èd a-be Thy name; For ev - er, for ev - er, for ev-er and ev - er,

ff

Hal-low-èd a-be Thy name. A - men, A-men, A - men, A - men,

ff

Ped. ✻ *Ped.* ✻

Hal-low-èd a-be Thy name; A - men, A-men, A - men, A-men,

Ped. ✻ *Ped.* ✻

poco rit.

Hal-low-èd a-be Thy name.

ff

Ped. ✻ *Ped.* ✻ *Ped.* ✻

Were you there?

Arranged by H.A.C.

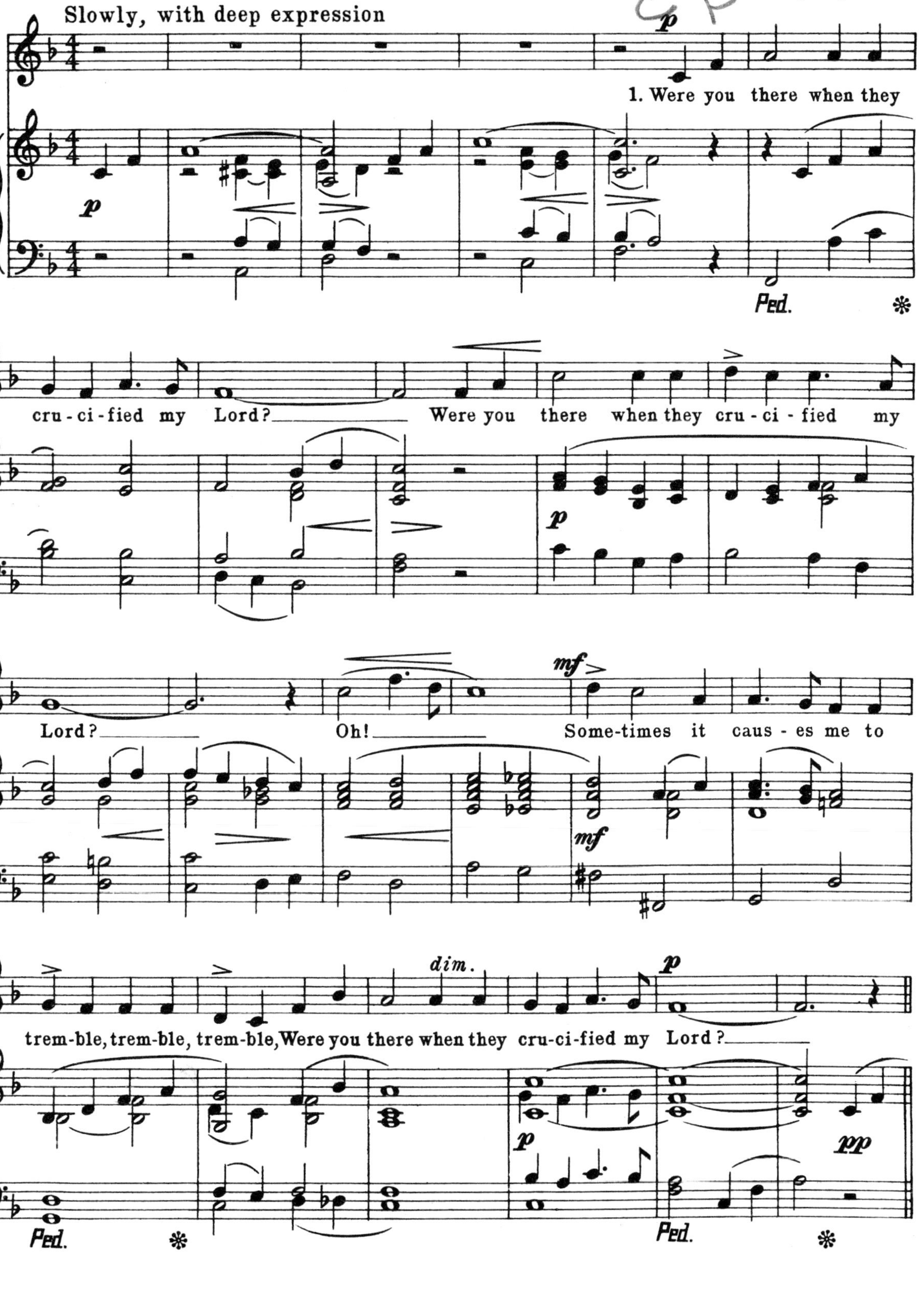

mp
2. Were you there when they laid him in the tomb?
3. Were you there when they rolled a-way the stone?
pp
sempre p
Were you there when they laid him in the tomb?
Were you there when they rolled a-way the stone?
mf
Oh!
Some-times it caus-es me to trem-ble, trem-ble, trem-ble, Were you there when they
ten.
dim.
Ped.
rall.
laid him in the tomb?
rolled a-way the stone?
D. S.
ppp
Ped.

Be still and listen

Male Quartet and Piano*

Words and music by PAUL HOGUE (1941)

Sometimes I feel so lonely, Sometimes I feel so blue,— Sometimes my heart's near break-in', Oh Lord, what shall I do?— Now I woke up dis

*The accompaniment need not be used except when the song is sung as a solo

Copyright, 1949, by The Oxford Group, 4, Hays Mews, London, W.1.

morn - in', I hate to face duh day, An' den I ope'd the Ho - ly Book, An'
pp
dis is what he say, Be still and lis - ten, Be still and lis - ten,
pp
pp
Be still and lis - ten Till duh still small voice comes through.

Duh Good Book says duh se-cret's To share my bro-ther's fears,— When I help bear my bro-ther's load My own woe dis-ap-pears.— I be still ev-'ry morn-ing, I lis-ten all duh day,— An' when I hear dat still small voice— 'Tsimport-ant to o - bey.__ Be still and lis-ten,_____ Be still and lis-ten,_____

Be still and lis-ten,_____ Till duh still small voice comes through.

I've a vis - ion for duh fu - ture, A heav'n on earth I see,—

Ped.   *Ped. simile*

When all folks live the list-'ning way— A hea-ven it will be.—

Slower Be still and lis-ten,——— Be still and lis-ten,———

Be still and lis-ten,——— *Very slow* Till duh still small voice comes through.

Ol' man Devil gotta go some

Words by CECIL BROADHURST
Music by RICHARD M. HADDEN (1952)

Broad and heavy

Brok-en-heart-ed world, Brok-en-heart-ed chil-dren, Mend the brok-en-heart in her chil-dren, Den you mend a brok-en-heart-ed world. *Faster, in free time* Dev-il in the world, Dev-il in her chil-dren, Chase the dev-il out of her chil-dren, Den you

Copyright, 1952, by M.R.A. Inc., 640, Fifth Avenue, New York City, U.S.A.

rit.
Agitated
chase the dev-il from the world! Dev-il run-nin' fast,
dim.
Dev-il gon-na catch you! Dev-il gon-na catch you if you
rall.
ten.
a tempo
don't mend your ways! Dev-il run-nin' fast, Dev-il gon-na catch you!
Dev-il gon-na catch you if you don't mend your ways!

Moderately fast, very rhythmical
Ol' Man Dev - il got-ta go some, Got - ta go some, Got - ta go some, go some,
Ol' Man Dev - il got-ta go some, If he's ev-er gon-na catch up to me!
Ol' Man Dev - il got-ta go some, Got - ta
mf
simile

go some, Got - ta go some, go some, Ol' Man Dev - il got - ta go some, If he's ev - er gon - na catch up to me! He'll need

poco accel.

light - nin' shoes, An' sil - ver wings, A can - non ball suit on, An' all those things! He'll need stream - line hat, An' high oc - tane, An'

a tempo
twent-y times speed_ of a hot jet plane! Ol' Man Dev - il got-ta
cresc.
go some, Got - ta go some, Got - ta go some, go some, Ol' Man Dev - il got-ta
cresc.
go some, If he's ev-er gon-na catch up to me!
L.H.
Ped.

Restitution

Arranged for Male Quartet
by DWIGHT BOILEAU

Words and music by PAUL HOGUE (1946)

Free time, in narrative style, with humour

2nd TENOR (Melody): Oh, Re-sti-tu-tion,— Re-sti-tu-tion, It's a great, great doc-trine like de Con-sti-tu-tion. If ya stole a-ny gold— or told a-ny lies, To git dat peace— ya got-ta 'po-la-gize!

* The accompaniment need not be used except when the song is sung as a solo

Copyright, 1949, by The Oxford Group, 4, Hays Mews, London, W.1.

Now Josh-ua done de-feat-ed town o' Je-ri-cho, Be-cause he walked de way de Lawd had tole him to go. But de Lawd said, "Don' ya steal none o' dat sil-ber or gold___ Or a-ny doom-ed thing with-in de e-ne-my's fold". But A-chan, one o' Josh-ua's sol-diers, shame de day *(Spoken)* He dis-o-beyed de Lawd in a most thiev-in-ish way. A

Ba-by-lon-ish robe an' gold he stole an' he hid, Not think-ing fer a mo-ment ob de sin dat he did.__ Oh, Re-sti-tu-tion, Re-sti-tu-tion, It's a great, great doc-trine like de Con-sti-tu-tion. If ya stole a-ny gold___ or told a-ny lies, To git dat peace ya got-ta 'po-la-gize!

Den Josh-ua he got sick an' den he want-ed to die,— 'Cause his ar-my got de-feat-ed by de King of Ai,— But de

trou - ble was with A - chan an duh loot in his tent,___ Ol'
A - chan nev - er thought he'd ev - er have to re - pent.___ But de
Lawd said to Josh-ua, "If you want to be blessed, Some - bo - dy in your ar-my's gon-na

gliss.

have to con-fess; A sin-ner's dis-o-beyed de word de Lawd has told, An' in de bot-tom of his tent he's got some stol-en gold!" Oh, Re-sti-tu-tion, Re-sti-tu-tion, It's a great, great doc-trine like de Con-sti-tu-tion. If ya stole a-ny gold ___ or told a-ny lies, To git dat peace ya got-ta 'po-la-gize! So Josh-ua took his ar-my, clan by clan, An' he ques-tioned ev-'ry fa-mi-ly, man by man, An' den he 'splained to A-chan 'bout de

mf
tra - ge - dy,—
Den
BARITONE
f
"Now tell me what ya done, an' don' ya hide it from me!"
(Spoken)
A - chan he con-fessed a-bout de loot he had stole,
"You'll find de loot an' mon-ey in my
1st TENOR
mf
mf (Hum)
(Spoken)
mf
tr
So Josh - ua sent his mes-sen-gers to A - chan's tent,-
tent, in a hole".
Dey
BASS
mf (Hum)
(Spoken)
mf
tr

found dat loot an' gold, an' A-chan sho did re-pent!* Oh, Re-sti-tu-tion, Re-sti-tu-tion, It's a great, great doc-trine like de Con-sti-tu-tion. If ya stole a-ny gold ___ or told a-ny lies, To git dat peace ya got-ta

*At this point bass runs finger across throat, with an appropriate noise, indicating Achans' fate!

'po-la-gize! Now with all de wrongs put right and full con-fes-sion made, De Is-rael-ites was rea-dy for dat Vic-t'ry Pa-rade! Josh-ua gath-ered all his war-riors, with their ban-ners on high, Den dey

molto pp
ten. dim.
mis-erb-ly de-feat-ed de ol' King of Ai! — Oh! Re - sti-tu - tion,
ten. molto dim.
pp
Re - sti-tu-tion, It's a great, great doc-trine like de Con - sti-tu - tion. If ya
sf
stole a-ny gold — or told a-ny lies, To git dat peace ya got-ta 'po-la-gize.
f
pp lunga
mp
ppp
slow gliss.
lunga

Ride on, King Jesus!

Arranged by HALL JOHNSON

Maestoso moderato

Ride on, King Jesus! No man can-a hin-der me. Ride on, King Je-sus, ride on! No man can-a hin-der me.

Stesso tempo

For He is King of kings, He is Lord of lords, Je-sus Christ, de first an las', No man works like Him. For He is

same breath

Copyright 1951 by Carl Fischer, Inc., New York
Reprinted by permission

King of kings, He is Lord of lords, Jesus Christ, de first an' las', No man works like Him. King Jesus rides a milk-white horse, No man works like Him. De river of Jerdin He did cross, No man works like Him. For He is King of kings, Lord of lords, Oh, Jesus Christ, de first an' las', Oh! *(same breath)* King

Jesus rides in de middle o' de air, Oh! He

calls de saints from everywhere, Ah!

Ride on, King Jesus! No man can a

114

rall. molto
f broaden *lunga* **ff**

Je - sus Christ, de first an' las', No man works like

a tempo faster

Him! Ride on, ride on,

ride on, ride on, Je - sus! cut

short

Roll away that stone

Words and music by RICHARD M. HADDEN (Easter, 1947)

Arranged by FRANCES ROOTS HADDEN

Copyright 1952 by Richard M. Hadden

out! They set a watch to keep Him in, Jus' like folks do to-day, But the an-gel came with ser-a-phim And rolled the stone a-way.

accel.

Slightly faster
Sit up-on that stone, broth-er, Jus' like the an-gel

did. Oh yes, jus' sit up-on that stone, broth-er, Jus' like the an - gel did. When John and Pe - ter went in-side, New hopes were there con - ceived, For His clothes were neat - ly laid a - side, And both of them be -

accel.
With animation
lieved. Sit up-on that stone, broth-er, And
simile
give a might - y shout! Oh yes, jus' sit up-on that
sf
rit.
stone, broth-er, 'Cos Je - sus has come out! Then Thom - as said, "I'll
dim.
not believe un-til I tru-ly see," But Je - sus said, "How bless-ed they who be-
mp

allarg.
f Broadly
lieve be-fore they see." Roll a-way that stone, broth-er, And
f
simile
o - pen up your heart, Oh yes, jus' roll a-way that stone, broth-er, And
o - pen up_your heart. O - pen up your heart, broth-er, And let Lord Je - sus
pp sub.
pp sub.
in! Oh yes, jus' o - pen up your heart, brother, And let Lord Je - sus in!
ppp
ppp

To Louis Byles

The Glow Within

WILL REED (1941)

Not too slow

1. Oh, you've got-ta get a glo-ry In the work you do,— A Hal-le-lu-jah Chor-us In the heart of you, Paint or tell a sto-ry, Sing or shov-el coal, Oh, you've got-ta get a glo-ry Or the job lacks soul. O— Lord, give me a glo-ry, Is it much to give? For you've got-ta get a glo-ry Or you just don't live.

Copyright, 1941, by Will Reed

122

A little faster

2. The great, whose shin-ing la-bours Make our pul-ses throb, Were men who got a glo-ry In their dai - ly job. The bat-tle might be go-ry And the odds un-fair, But the men who got a glo-ry Nev-er knew des - pair. O— Lord, give me a glo-ry, When all else is done, If you've on-ly got a glo-ry You can still go on.

Tempo I

short pause

Joyful

3. For those who get a glo-ry It is like the sun,— And you can see it glow-ing Through the work they've done. O fame is trans-i-to-ry, Rich-es fade a-way— But when you've got-ta glo-ry It is there to stay. O— Lord, give me a glo-ry And a work-man's pride, For you've got-ta get a glo-ry Or you're dead in-side.

Trouble

Words and music by ROBERT MacGIMSEY

Copyright 1933 by Carl Fischer, Inc., New York
Reprinted by permission

(with despair- fear) — Trou-ble all Ah see,—— Keep fol-low-in' me, keep fol-low-in' me,——

(weak, hopeless) Keep fol-low in' me,—— fol-low-in' me.

(dying away)

* Repetition of these last ten measures is optional.

INTRODUCTION AND ACKNOWLEDGMENTS

This Lowes Foods Recipe Book contains a wealth of practical information for both new and experienced cooks. We've created it to ease the dinner dilemma on busy weeknights. We hope that it will help you plan and prepare countless meals for your family and friends, and that it will become a trusted and valued kitchen resource.

This book was written and edited by

Dianne Blancato and Cindy Silver, MS, RD, LDN.

We thank Betsy Fitzmaurice and Jennifer Hale, dietetic interns at UNC-Greensboro, for their assistance.

Copyright 2008 Lowe's Food Stores, Inc., North Carolina

All rights reserved. No part of this book can be reproduced in any form, or by any means, in another book without the written permission of the publisher and Lowe's Foods, Inc., except when permitted by law.

ISBN: 978-0-9626682-5-8

Published by Dockery House Publishing, Inc.
P.O. Box 1237, Lindale, Texas 75771. Phone: 903-882-6900.

Dockery House Publishing

Rodney L. Dockery	Publisher
Caleb Pirtle III	Creative Director
Kim Dockery	Vice President/ Business Development
Kim Phillips	Art Director
Jutta Medina	Graphic Design

Manufactured in the United States of America

First Printing

Table of Contents

Introduction and Acknowledgments	page 1
Table of Contents	page 2
Pork Nutrition and Good For You Choices	page 3
Pork Cuts	page 4
Cooking Methods	page 5
Basic Cookware	page 6 - 8
Quick Tips	page 9
Food Safety	page 10 - 11
All Purpose Rubs	page 12
Marinades	page 13
Pork Recipes with Meal Suggestions	page 14
Index	page 95
About Lowes Foods	page 96

Pork Nutrition

Fresh pork is an important food that supplies us with complete protein, minerals, vitamins, fat and saturated fat. Complete protein is high in quality and helps the body grow and function properly. Pork is a good source of the mineral, zinc. It is also a good source of the vitamin, thiamin, which is a B-vitamin. In addition to these positive nutrients, there is also fat and saturated fat in pork. Due to the fact that eating too much total fat can be a risk for obesity, and too much saturated fat can be a risk for heart disease, it is recommended to consume fresh pork in a moderate portion. A 3-4 ounce portion of cooked pork, which is the size of one deck of cards, is moderate and it helps complete a meal with other healthful dishes.

The leanest cuts of fresh pork are those which are lowest in total fat and saturated fat. It is easy to choose lean cuts such as tenderloin, center cut loin chops, and loin roast. Due to the fact that lean, fresh pork tends to be tougher, it is helpful to tenderize, marinate and/or slow cook these cuts for a tender, cooked meal.

Note: Cured and smoked meats, such as ham, bacon, Canadian bacon and smoked pork chops, have a considerably higher sodium (salt) content than fresh pork.

Good For You Choices

As you use this cookbook you may want to choose pork recipes that are best for a healthy lifestyle. Look for this symbol 🍏 for choices that are lower in calories, fat, saturated fat, sodium, and/or higher in fiber. Healthy nutrient amounts are listed in bold type and the more bold nutrients in a recipe, the healthier it is. To qualify as healthy, one serving of a recipe contains ≤300 calories, ≤10 gm total fat, ≤3 gm saturated fat, ≤350 mg sodium, or ≥3 gm fiber. The 🍏 in the Index indicates recipes with 2 or more healthy, bolded nutrients.

Cuts of Pork

Steaks
(1) Boston Butt

    Preferred cooking methods: Grill, sauté, braise

Roasts

(1) Boston Butt
(2) Boneless Center Cut Loin
(2) Tenderloin*

    Preferred cooking methods: Grill, broil, roast, braise, sauté
    *Also may be stir-fried

Chops

(2) Center Cut Rib
(2) Center Cut Loin
(2) Boneless Center Cut Loin*

    Preferred cooking methods: Grill, broil, braise, sauté
    *Also may be stir-fried

Ribs

(1) Bone-in Southern Style
(2) Loin Country Style
(5) Spare
(2) Baby Back

    Preferred cooking methods: Grill, roast

Other

(1) Pork Stew

    Preferred cooking methods: Stew, braise

(1) Ground

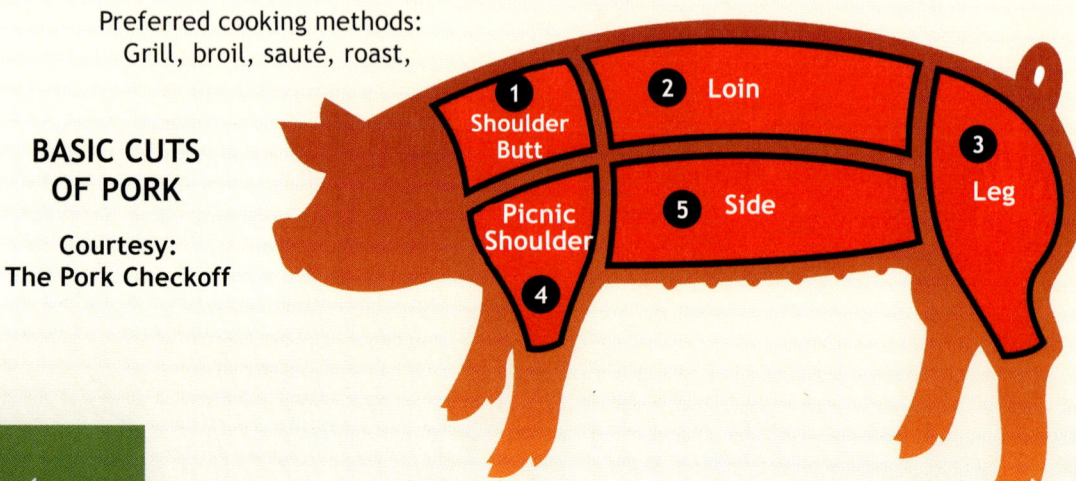

    Preferred cooking methods:
    Grill, broil, sauté, roast,

BASIC CUTS OF PORK

Courtesy:
The Pork Checkoff

1. Shoulder Butt
2. Loin
3. Leg
4. Picnic Shoulder
5. Side

Cooking Methods

Broil – Cooking food directly under the oven heat source.

Braise – A cooking method that involves browning meat in oil or other fat and then cooking slowly in liquid. The result of braising is to tenderize the meat.

Brown – Quickly sautéing, pan/oven broiling, or grilling done either at the beginning or end of meal preparation, often to enhance flavor, texture, or eye appeal.

Grill – Using an outdoor gas or charcoal grill to cook meat on top of the heat source. This can also be done on the stovetop with a grill pan.

Microwave – Best used to thaw frozen meat quickly or reheat leftover meat. Not recommended for cooking fresh meat, as it can cause the meat to become tough.

Oven bag - A heat durable bag used to cook meats in a roasting pan in the oven. This allows meat to cook more quickly.

Roast – Cooking meat uncovered in the oven in a heavy, metal roasting pan.

Sauté – Cooking food quickly in a small amount of oil in a skillet or sauté pan over direct heat.

Sear - Sealing in a meat's juices by cooking it quickly under very high heat.

Skillet cooking – Using a skillet or frying pan to cook meat on a stovetop.

Stir-frying – Cooking meat that is cut into pieces with a small amount of oil, over high heat, using a deep fry pan or wok and wooden or metal utensils.

Stew – Cooking less tender cuts of meat for a long time in a small amount of liquid. This can be done on the stove, in the oven, in a slow-cooker or crock-pot.

Slow-cooking (crock pot cooking) – Using an electric slow cooker (or crock pot) to cook meat for a long period of time at a low temperature.

Basic Cookware, Knives and Utensils

Cookware

12 inch skillet – Stainless steel and non-stick - Used for general stovetop cooking (sautéing, browning, stir-frying).

3 quart saucepan - Used for general stovetop cooking (boiling, simmering, re-heating).

2 quart saucepan - Used for general stovetop cooking (boiling, simmering, re-heating).

6 quart stock pot – Used on the stovetop for making soup, stew or stock.

Dutch Oven – A heavy cooking pot used for cooking soup, or stew. Used on the stove top and in the oven.

Slow-cooker (or crock pot) – An electrical pot used to cook meats at low temperatures for a long period of time.

Broiler Pan – A rectangular, 2-part pan used to cook meat in the oven broiler. The upper pan is slotted to allow meat juices to drip to the lower pan which is solid.

Grill – Used to cook meat at high temperatures with the heat source underneath it. Grilling also contributes flavor to the meat.

Roasting pan – A rectangular, metal pan used to roast meats in the oven.

Knives

Paring knife, 2 to 4 inches – Used for cutting and delicate tasks such as removing the skin from tomatoes or peaches.

Utility knife, 6 to 8 inches – Used for cutting fruits and vegetables.

Chef's knife, 8 to 14 inches - Used for chopping, slicing, and mincing.

Steak knife – Used for cutting meat at the dining table.

BASIC COOKWARE, KNIVES AND UTENSILS

UTENSILS

Tongs – Kitchen and grill tongs - Used to grasp hot foods.

Solid spoons – Used for stirring foods.

Slotted spoons – Used for straining foods.

Ladles – Used for serving soups and stews, or for transferring liquids.

Whisk –Used to hand beat, blend and stir liquid or liquid-like ingredients.

Spatula –A flat metal, plastic or rubber utensil with a handle used to scrape mixtures from pots and bowls. Also used in folding together or turning ingredients.

Garlic press – A plastic or metal tool that presses a clove of garlic through small holes. Used when a recipe calls for minced garlic.

Kitchen shears – Used for cutting tasks such as snipping fresh herbs, cutting butcher's twine or splitting the breast bone of a chicken.

Vegetable peeler – Used to shave the outer peel of fruits and vegetables.

Marinade brush – Used to apply marinades or sauces to meats or vegetables while grilling.

Barbecue mitt – Long, flame resistant mitten designed to protect the hand and forearm from high heat while grilling.

Barbecue utensil set – Grilling utensils with insulated handles to protect the hand from high heat while grilling. Handles are long for easier turning of meat.

Citrus juicer –Used to break up the fibers of citrus fruits which releases their juice.

Citrus zester – Used to finely grate the top layer of the citrus peel or zest when it is called for in a recipe, marinade or sauce.

BASIC COOKWARE, KNIVES AND UTENSILS

UTENSILS

Measuring spoons – Used to measure precise amounts of liquid or dry ingredients.

Dry measuring cups – Used to measure precise amounts of dry ingredients such as flour or sugar.

Liquid measuring cups – Used to measure precise amounts of liquid ingredients such as water, milk, wine or juice.

Meat thermometer - Instant read and oven-safe - Used to determine the internal temperature of cooked meats. This is the most accurate and safest way to determine the doneness of meats. See the food safety section for more information on using a meat thermometer.

Timers – Used to ensure accurate cooking times.

Quick Tips

Choosing the Right Amount of Meat for your Recipe

When a recipe calls for a specific amount of meat, (for example, 1 pound Pork loin roast), you may find that the meat department does not have exactly 1 pound available. You can always buy a little over or a little under the specified amount. This will not change the amount of marinade or rub you will need, and it will not change the amount of time needed to cook the meat.

Letting Meat Rest

When meat is done cooking and has been removed from the heat, allow it to stand for 15 minutes. This will keep the meat moist by preventing its juices from running out onto your cutting board when you slice it.

Slicing Meat Against the Grain

When a recipe calls for slicing meat against the grain, look at the cooked meat and locate the direction of its string-like fibers (the grain). Slice the meat in the opposite direction of the grain to provide a tender slice of meat. If you cut the meat in the same direction as the grain, the result will be a chewy slice of meat.

Example: If the grain is going in a north/south direction then cut the slices in an east/west direction.

Using Cooked Meat Leftovers

- Slice and use in a sandwich or tortilla wrap
- Cut into small pieces and use in an omelet or breakfast casserole
- Slice and use in a salad
- Add to your favorite soup or chili
- Add to cooked pasta and steamed vegetables
- Add them as a topping for a frozen pizza

Food Safety

Storing Raw Pork

- Store in a refrigerator at 40° or lower.
- Store in a freezer at 0°.
- Store uncooked pork in refrigerator for 2-3 days.
- Store uncooked pork in freezer for 4-12 months.

Thawing Pork

- Thaw pork in the refrigerator at 40° or below. Allow 24-48 hours for every 5 pounds of frozen pork.
- Thaw pork in microwave if you are going to cook it immediately.
- Never thaw pork at room temperature.

Marinade Safety

- Marinade should be used the day it is prepared.
- To use a marinade as a sauce after the raw pork has marinated in it, rapidly boil the marinade for 1-2 minutes to destroy bacteria.

Using a Meat Thermometer

- Instant-read thermometer - Used after pork is cooked.
    Speed: Determines the temperature in 15-20 seconds.
    Placement: Insert thermometer 2-2 ½ inches deep into the thickest part of the pork. Do not touch bone with thermometer.

- Oven-safe thermometer – Used in the oven while pork is cooking.
    Speed: Determines temperature in 1-2 minutes.
    Placement: Insert thermometer 2-2 ½ inches deep into the thickest part of the pork. Do not touch bone with thermometer.

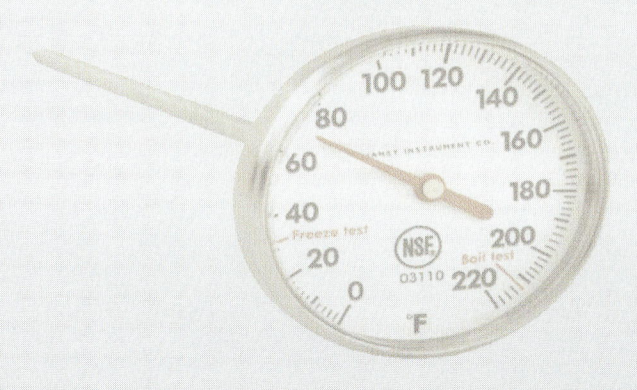

Food Safety

Storing Cooked Pork

- Refrigerate or freeze cooked pork in food grade storage containers with a lid, label and date.
- Store cooked pork in the refrigerator for 3-4 days.
- Store cooked pork in freezer for 2-3 months.
- Reheat cooked pork to a temperature of 165°.
    Stir mixed pork dishes frequently to ensure even reheating.

Doneness Temperatures for Meats

Use this guide when cooking meats. Always use a meat thermometer to determine doneness.

- Ground meats
    - Beef, veal, lamb, pork — 160°
    - Chicken, turkey — 165°

- Roasts and steaks (beef, veal, lamb)
    - Medium rare — 145°
    - Medium — 160°
    - Well-done — 170°

- Pork
    - Roasts, chops, ribs (medium) — 160°
    - Roasts, chops, ribs (well-done) — 170°
    - Ham, fresh — 160°
    - Sausage, fresh — 160°

ALL PURPOSE RUBS

- Each recipe makes 1/2 cup of rub.
- Use two tablespoons rub for every pound of meat.

Herb Rub
- 1 tablespoon Thyme
- 1 tablespoon Marjoram
- 1 tablespoon Sage
- 1 tablespoon Powdered basil
- 1 tablespoon Lemon zest

Italian Rub
- 4 tablespoons Onion powder
- 2 teaspoons Dried oregano
- 4 teaspoons Dried basil

Classic Rub
- 1 teaspoon White pepper
- 3 1/2 tablespoons Onion powder
- 1 tablespoon Garlic powder
- 1 1/2 tablespoons Dry mustard

Cajun Rub
- 2 tablespoons Paprika
- 2 teaspoons Salt
- 2 teaspoons Onion powder
- 2 teaspoons Garlic powder
- 1 teaspoon Cayenne pepper
- 1 teaspoon Ground white pepper
- 1/2 teaspoon Ground black pepper
- 1 teaspoon Dried thyme
- 1 teaspoon Dried oregano

Exotic Rub
- 1 tablespoon Dry mustard
- 1 1/2 teaspoons White pepper
- 1 teaspoon Curry powder
- 3 tablespoons Onion powder
- 1/2 teaspoon Garlic powder

World Rub
- 5 teaspoons Onion powder
- 1 tablespoon Garlic powder
- 1 tablespoon Paprika
- 1 tablespoon Dry mustard
- 1 teaspoon Dried thyme
- 1/2 teaspoon White pepper

Tips

- Store leftover rub in a sealed, airtight container and keep in your spice cabinet for up to 6 months.

- Add leftover rub to sour cream for a raw vegetable dip or add it to cream cheese for a cracker or bagel spread.

- Add leftover rub to olive oil for a quick salad dressing or dipping sauce for bread.

MARINADES

- Each recipe makes 1 cup of marinade.
- Use 1/2 cup marinade for every pound of meat.

Savory Meat Marinade
    3/4 cup Vegetable oil
    1/4 cup Lemon juice
    2 tablespoons Chopped onion
    2 cloves Garlic, minced
    1 teaspoon Pepper

Citrus/Balsamic Marinade
    1/2 cup lemon juice
    1/4 cup Worcestershire Sauce
    3 tablespoons Balsamic vinegar
    3 tablespoons Olive oil
    2 teaspoons Garlic, finely chopped

Sweet Marinade
    1/3 cup Vegetable oil
    1/3 cup Reduced sodium soy sauce
    3 tablespoons Red wine vinegar
    2 tablespoons Chutney (or your favorite fruit jam)
    1 clove Garlic, minced
    1 small Onion, chopped

Rosemary Marinade
    1/2 cup Lemon juice
    1/2 cup Olive oil
    4 cloves Garlic, minced
    3 tablespoons Rosemary, minced (or 1 1/2 tablespoons dried)
    1 teaspoon salt

Teriyaki Marinade
    1/2 cup Reduced-sodium soy sauce
    2 tablespoons Onion, chopped
    3 tablespoons Vegetable oil
    2 tablespoons Rice vinegar
    2 tablespoons Honey
    1 clove Garlic, minced
    2 teaspoons Ginger, minced

Pineapple Marinade
    3/4 cup Crushed pineapple with juice
    1 clove Garlic, minced
    2 tablespoons Brown sugar
    1/3 cup Dry sherry
    1 teaspoon Dried rosemary, crumbled

Tips

- Marinade should be used the day it is prepared.

- To use a marinade as a sauce after the raw meat has marinated in it, rapidly boil the marinade for 1-2 minutes to destroy bacteria.

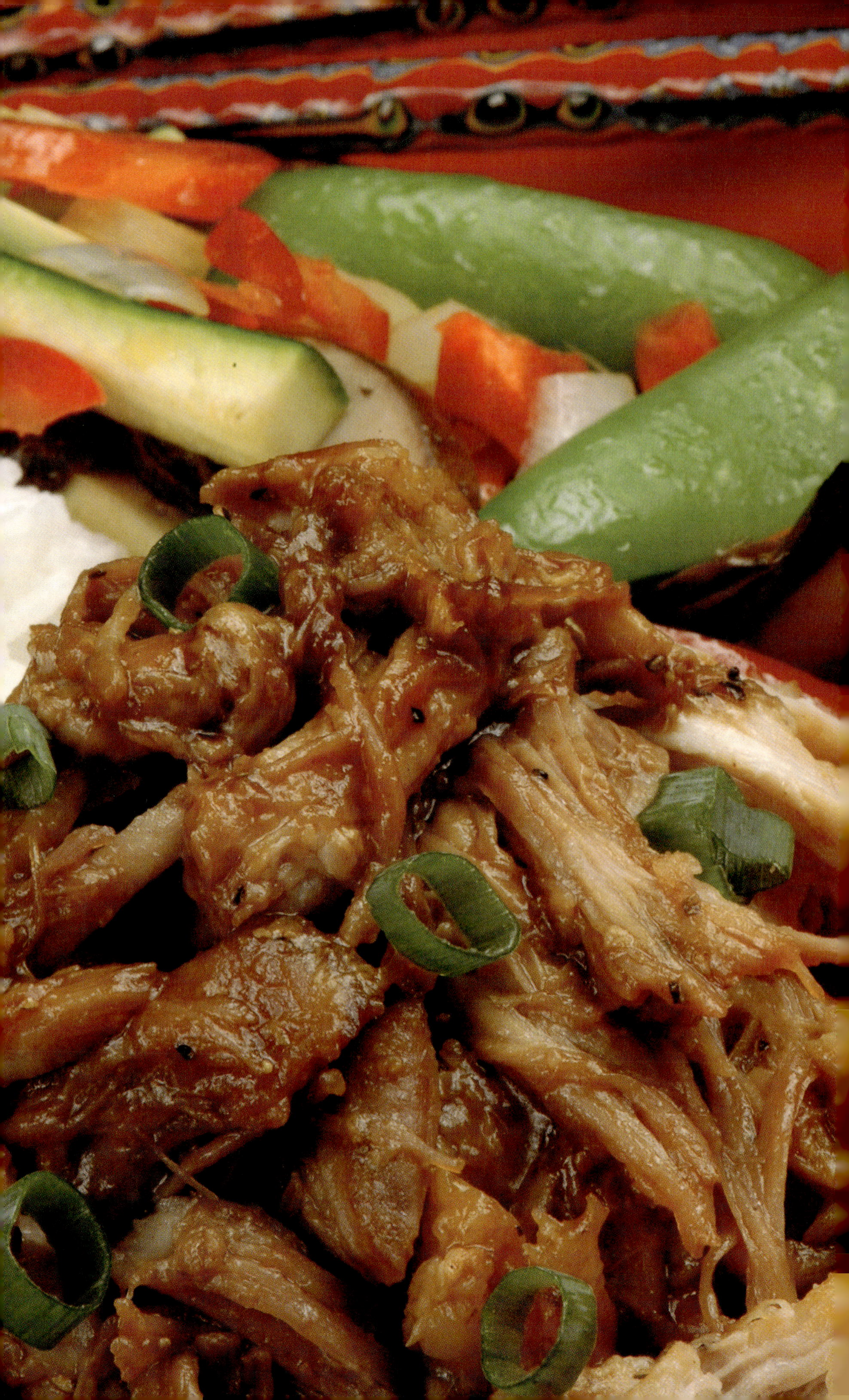

CHINESE-STYLE BARBECUED PORK

To reduce the fat content, refrigerate the sauce overnight and skim the fat off the next day. Warm the sauce and meat together in a large skillet.

Equipment Needed:

Slow-cooker or crock pot

Marinade:
1 cup Hoisin sauce
1 cup Reduced-sodium soy sauce
1/4 cup Rice wine vinegar
1/2 cup Honey
2 tablespoons Ginger, minced
4 cloves Garlic, minced
2 teaspoons Sesame oil
1 teaspoon Chinese five-spice powder
1/2 teaspoon Pepper
4 pounds Boston butt roast

Ideas for Making a Balanced Meal:

Serve with rice, green peas and sliced fresh kiwi

or

Serve with lightly buttered spaghetti and colorful, stir fried vegetables

1. Combine marinade ingredients in a medium bowl, stirring well with a whisk. Place in a gallon-sized zip-top plastic bag. Add pork to bag; seal. Marinate in refrigerator for 1-24 hours, turning occasionally.

2. Place pork and marinade in slow cooker. Cover and cook on HIGH for 3 hours, then turn to LOW for 6 hours, or until pork pulls apart with a fork.

3. Shred pork with 2 forks and serve with sauce.

Serves: 16

Recipe Nutrition per serving:

259 calories; 17 gm protein; 18 gm carbohydrates; 13 gm total fat; 5 gm saturated fat; 56 mg cholesterol; 1 gm fiber; 903 mg sodium.

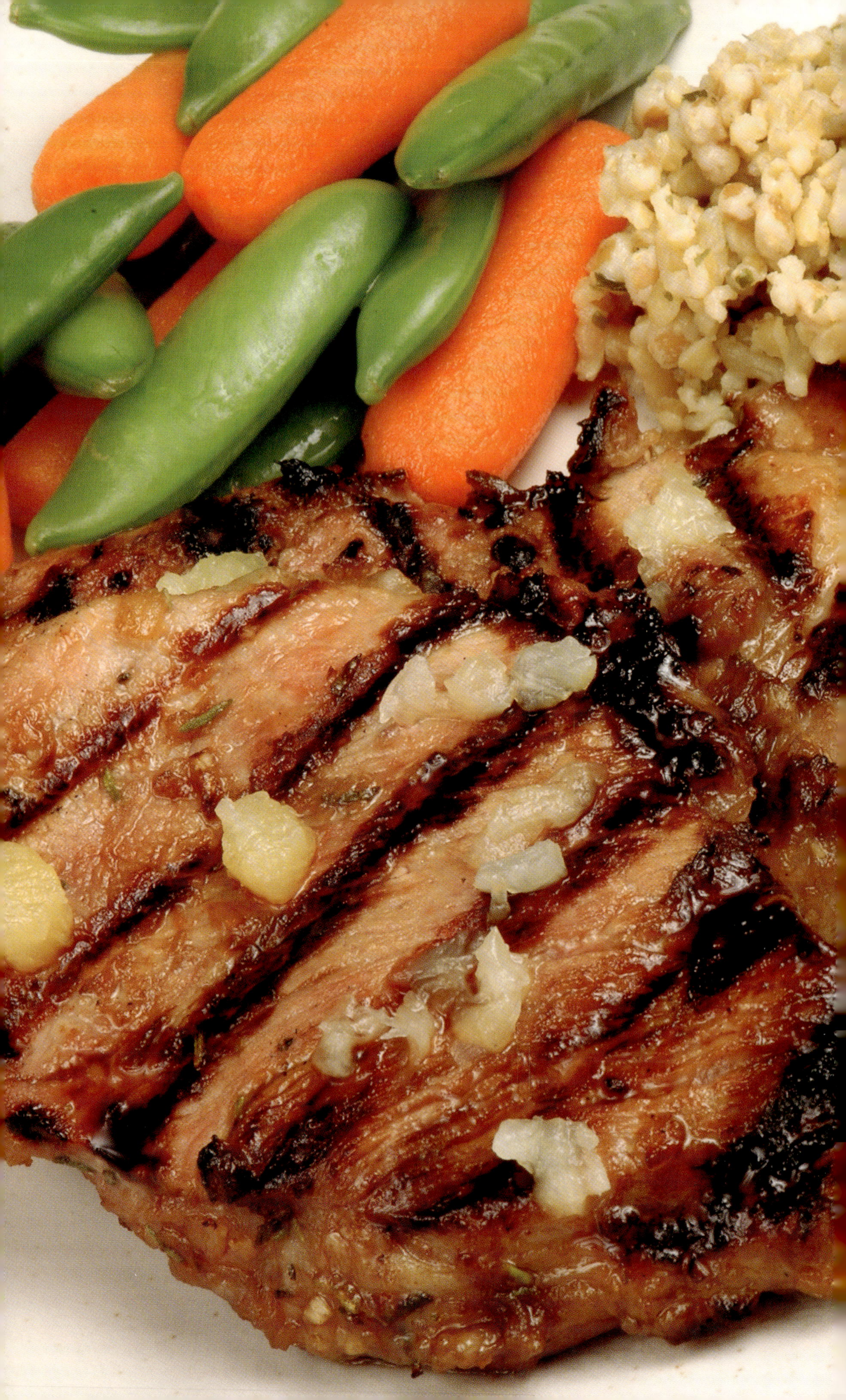

PINEAPPLE PORK STEAK

Try this recipe cut into strips on a salad or wrapped in a tortilla.

Equipment Needed:

Grill

1 1/2 pounds Boston butt steaks
3/4 cup Crushed pineapple, with juice
1/2 cup Dry sherry
2 tablespoons Brown sugar
1 clove Garlic, minced
1/2 teaspoon Rosemary

Ideas for Making a Balanced Meal:

Serve with a baked potato, green beans and fresh mango slices

or

Serve with rice pilaf, steamed sugar snap peas and a tossed salad

1. Place pork steaks in a zip-top plastic bag.

2. Combine remaining ingredients, and pour into bag. Seal bag, and refrigerate for 1-24 hours.

3. Grill over medium-high heat 18-20 minutes, or until meat thermometer reaches 160°.

Serves: 6

Recipe Nutrition per serving:

255 calories; 22 gm protein; 7 gm carbohydrates; 14 gm total fat; 5 gm saturated fat; 81 mg cholesterol; 0 gm fiber; **60 mg sodium**.

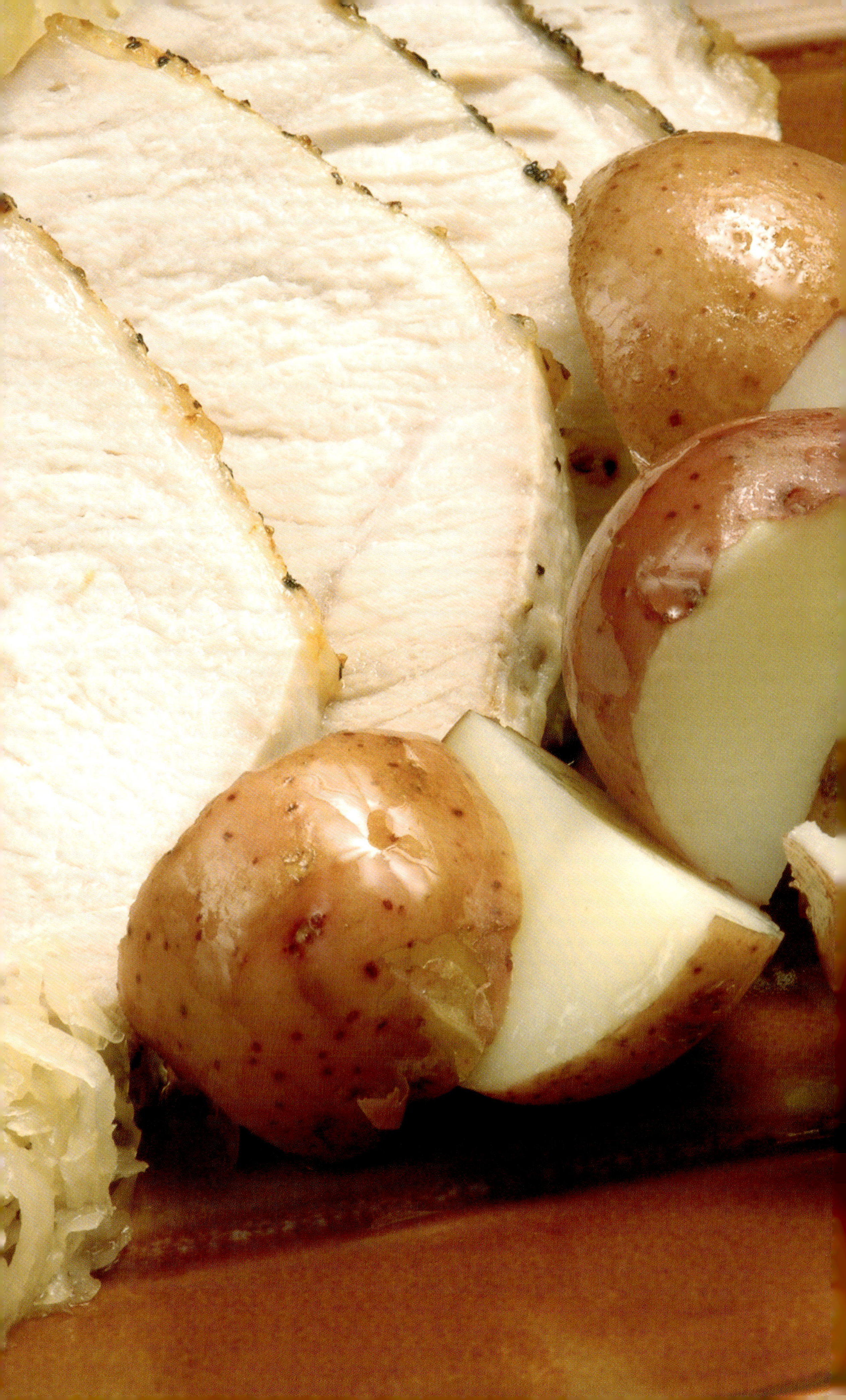

GERMAN-STYLE PORK ROAST

Use leftovers of this tasty roast in a sandwich on rye bread.

Equipment Needed:

Roasting pan

4 pounds Pork loin roast
1 tablespoon Sugar
3/4 teaspoon Caraway seeds
1/4 teaspoon Salt
2 cups Apple Juice

1 tablespoon Lemon Juice
1/2 teaspoon Peppercorns
2 Bay leaves
1 jar, 32 ounces, Sauerkraut
1 1/2 cups Apple, chopped

Ideas for Making a Balanced Meal:

Serve with mashed potatoes and fresh steamed asparagus
or
Serve with warm dark pumpernickel bread and spinach salad

1. Place pork in slow-cooker and add the juice from the sauerkraut, sugar, caraway seeds, salt, apple juice, lemon juice, peppercorns and bay leaves. Cook on low for 1 hour.

2. Add sauerkraut and apple. Continue to cook on low for 6 hours, or until tender.

Serves: 12

Recipe Nutrition per serving:

313 calories; 31 gm protein; 12 gm carbohydrates; 15 gm total fat; 6 gm saturated fat; 91 mg cholesterol; **3 gm fiber**; 621 mg sodium.

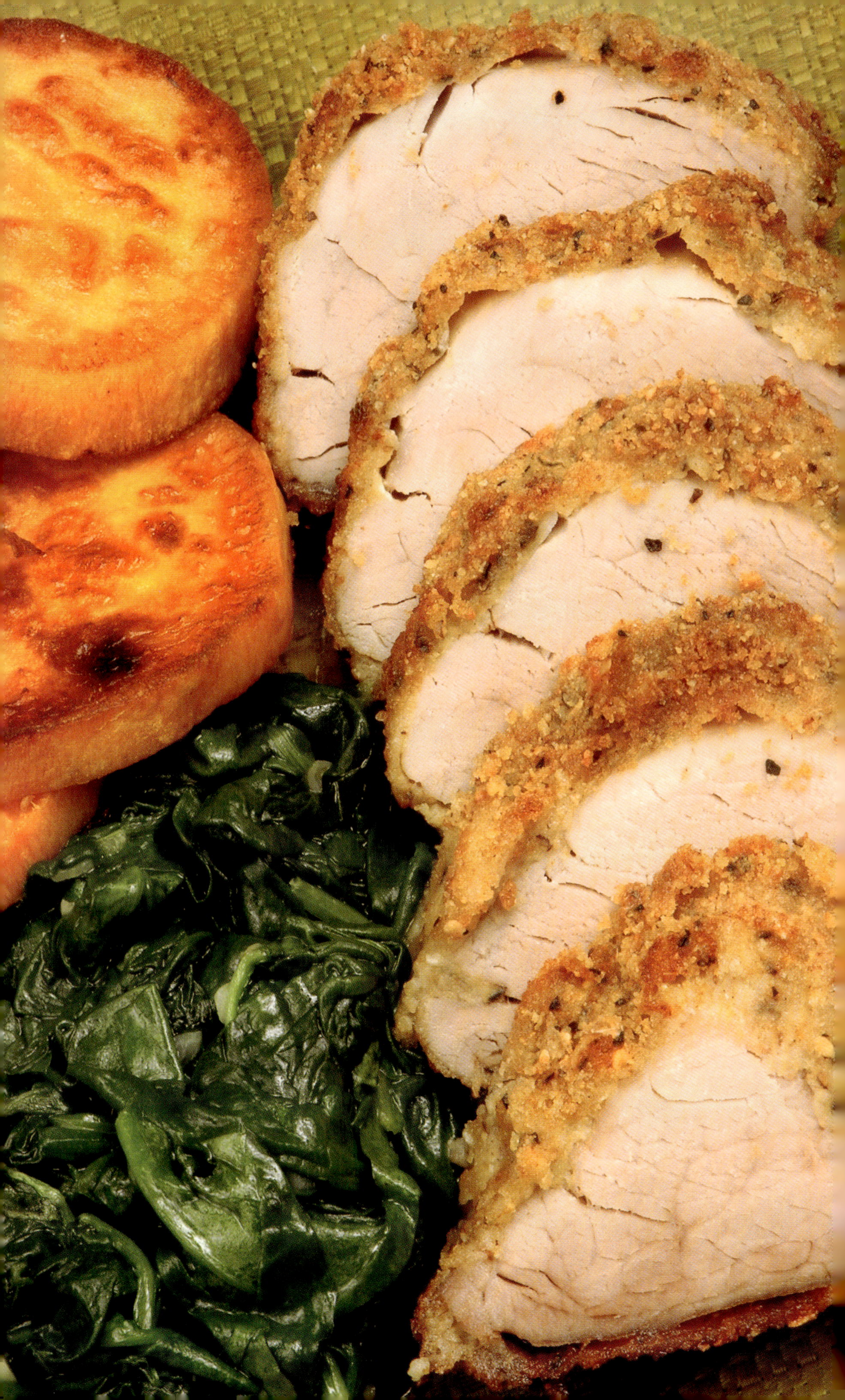

Parmesan Crusted Pork

Children enjoy the process of preparing this tasty recipe.

Equipment Needed:

Roasting pan

1 cup Plain bread crumbs
1/4 cup Parmesan cheese, grated
1 teaspoon Dried Thyme
1/4 teaspoon Salt
1/2 teaspoon Pepper

2 pounds Pork tenderloin
1 Egg, beaten
3 tablespoons Butter, melted

Ideas for Making a Balanced Meal:

Serve with quick cooking wild rice mix and tomato-cucumber vinaigrette salad

or

Serve with a sweet potato and steamed spinach

1. Combine bread crumbs, cheese, thyme, salt and pepper in a shallow dish.

2. Dip pork in egg, then in bread crumb mixture.

3. Place pork in roasting pan sprayed with cooking spray. Drizzle with melted butter.

4. Bake at 425° for about 25 minutes or until meat thermometer registers 160°. Cover with foil after taking out of the oven and let stand for 5 minutes.

Serves: 8

Recipe Nutrition per serving:

234 calories; 25 gm protein; 10 gm carbohydrates; **10 gm total fat**; 4 gm saturated fat; 100 mg cholesterol; 1 gm fiber; **302 mg sodium**.

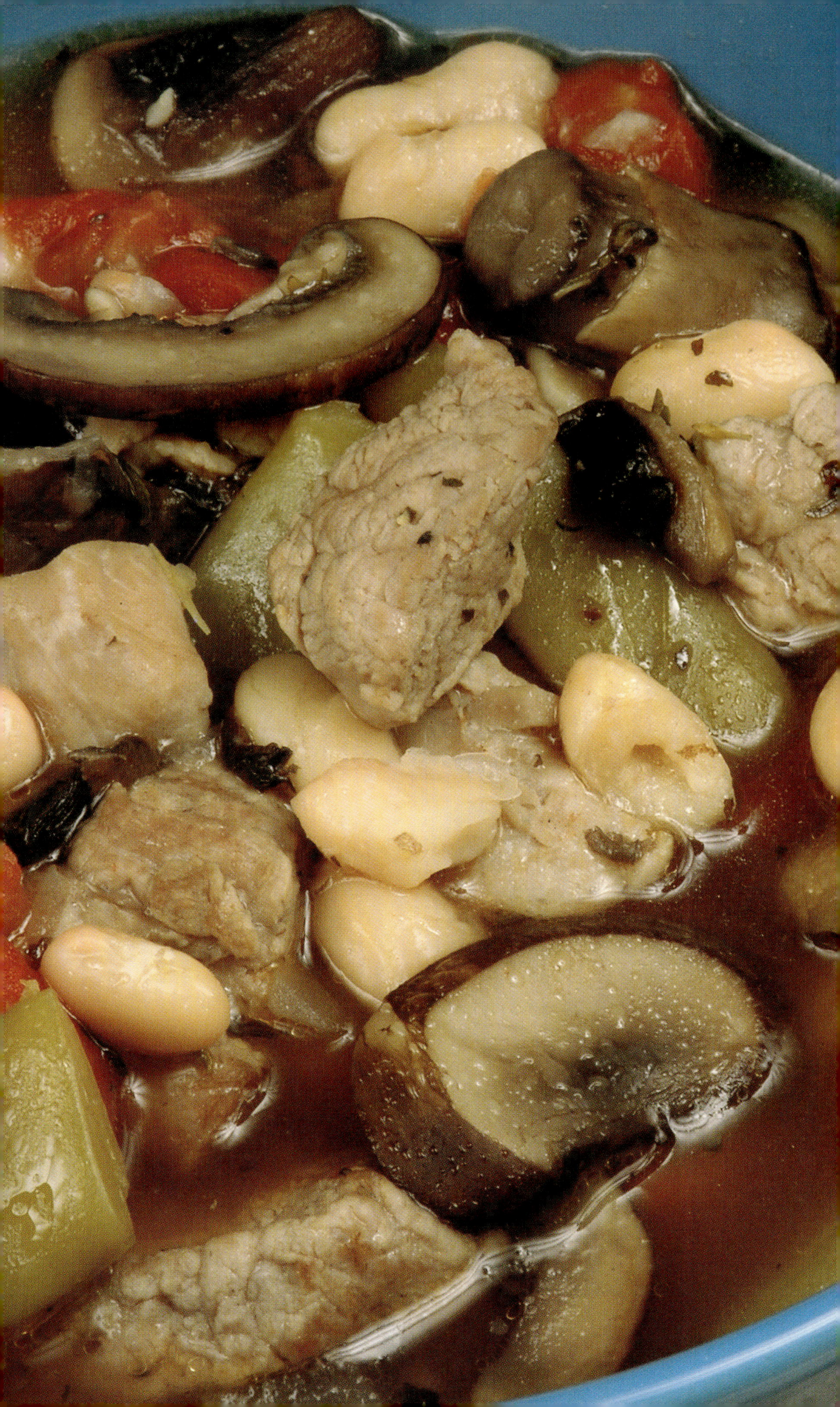

PORK VEGETABLE SOUP

Try this hearty soup on a cool fall day.

Equipment Needed:

6-quart pot

1 tablespoon Olive oil
1 pound Pork tenderloin, cut into 1/2 inch pieces
8 ounces Mushrooms, sliced
1 large Red onion, chopped
1/4 teaspoon Salt
1/4 teaspoon Pepper
4 cups Reduced-sodium chicken broth
1 cup Water
1 can, 28 ounces, Diced tomatoes
2 cloves Garlic, minced
1 package, 16 ounces, Italian green beans, frozen
1 can, 15 ounces, Great northern beans
2 teaspoons Italian seasoning
1/4 teaspoon Cayenne pepper

Ideas for Making a Balanced Meal:

Serve with a crusty, whole grain roll and mixed fruit salad

or

Serve with a large tossed salad and crackers

1. Heat oil in a 6-quart pot over medium-high heat. Sauté pork, mushrooms, onion, salt and pepper for 4 minutes.

2. Add broth, water, tomatoes, garlic, green beans, Great Northern beans, Italian seasoning and cayenne pepper.

3. Reduce heat to medium-low and cook until heated through, about 20-30 minutes.

Serves: 10

Recipe Nutrition per serving:

165 calories; 16 gm protein; 19 gm carbohydrates; **4 gm total fat**; **1 gm saturated fat**; 24 mg cholesterol; **6 gm fiber**; 497 mg sodium.

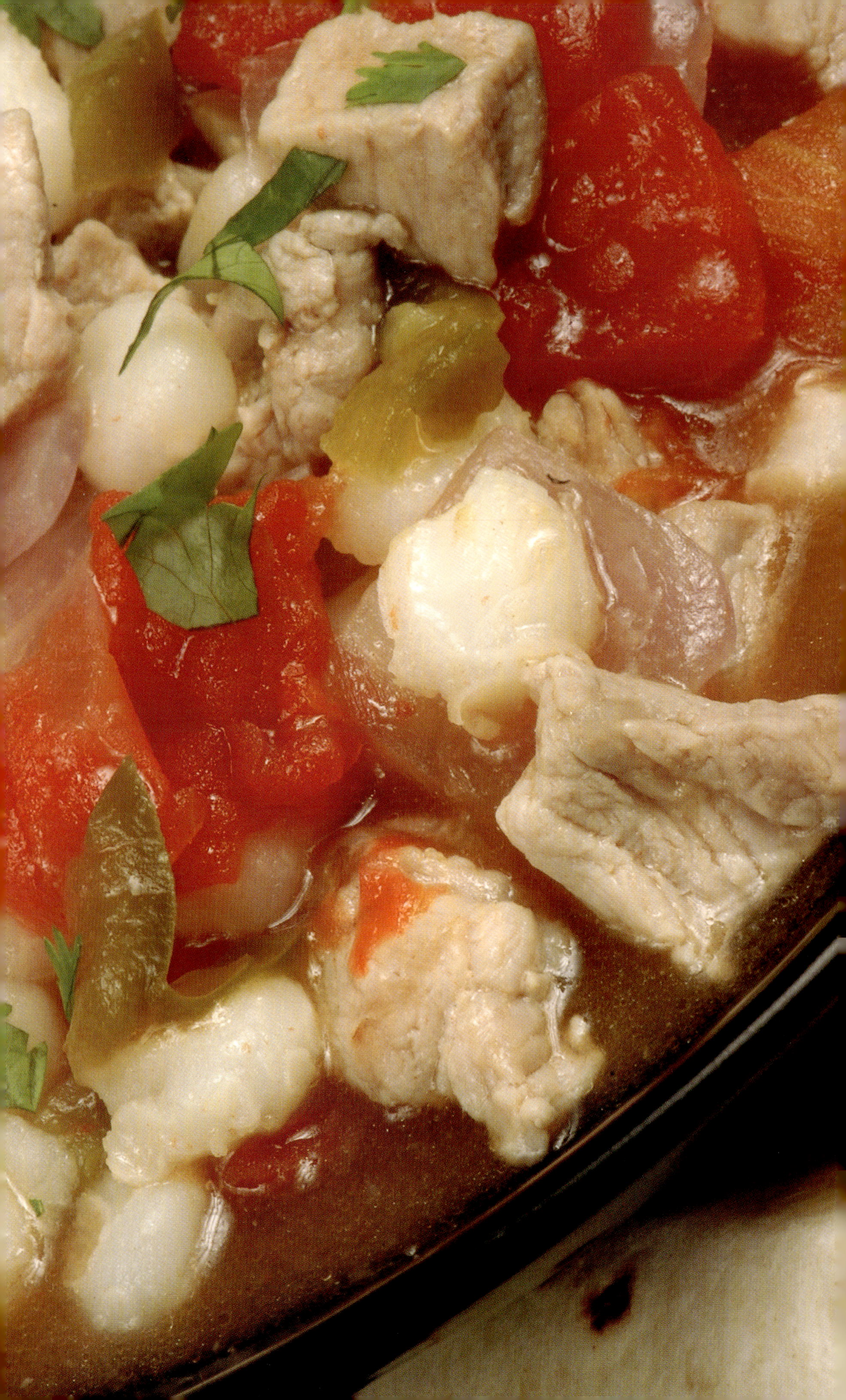

Pork and Hominy Soup

Serve this Mexican style soup for something different.

Equipment Needed:

Dutch oven or 6-quart pot

2 tablespoons Vegetable oil
3 pounds Pork tenderloin, cut into 1/2-inch pieces
4 cloves Garlic, chopped
2 cups Onion, chopped
1 can, 28 ounces, Diced tomatoes
6 cups Chicken broth
2 Jalapeño peppers, seeded and chopped
1 can, 30 ounces, Hominy, drained
1/2 teaspoon Salt
1/2 Lime, juiced

Garnishes:
1/2 cup Fresh Cilantro, chopped
1/4 cup Reduced-fat sour cream

Ideas for Making a Balanced Meal:

Serve with fresh crusty bread and a shredded carrot salad

or

Serve with grainy crackers, thinly sliced cheese and a fresh sliced pear

1. Heat the oil in a large pot over medium-high heat. Add pork, garlic and onion, and cook 5 minutes, stirring occasionally.

2. Add tomatoes, broth, peppers, hominy and salt; bring to a boil and immediately reduce heat to low. Simmer for 30 minutes.

3. Add lime juice to soup and stir.

4. Serve with cilantro and sour cream.

Serves: 8

Recipe Nutrition per serving:

360 calories; 39 gm protein; 24 gm carbohydrates; 11 gm total fat; **3 gm saturated fat**; 92 mg cholesterol; **3 gm fiber**; 1297 mg sodium.

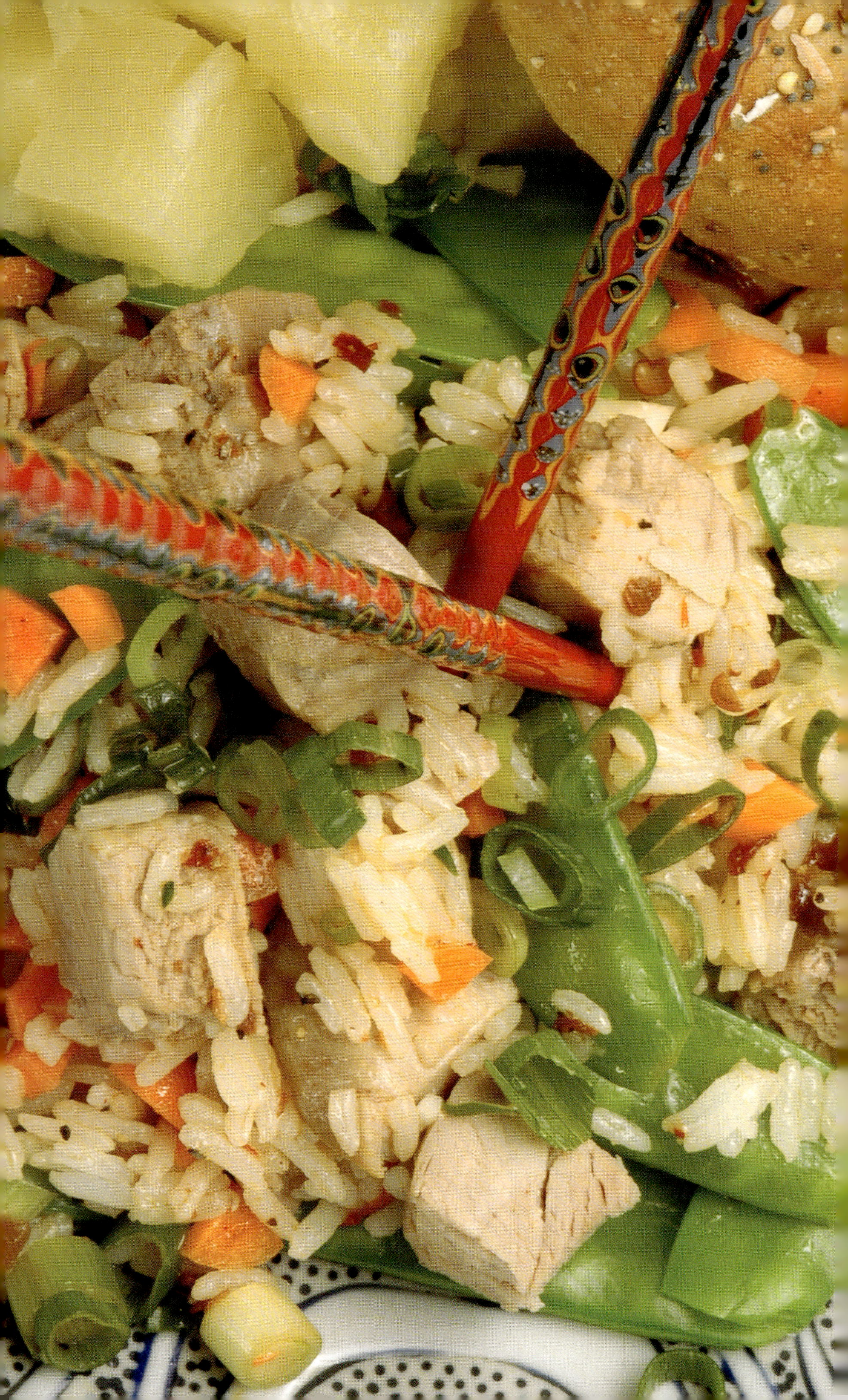

ASIAN PORK AND RICE SALAD

This makes an easy and colorful one-dish meal.

Equipment Needed:

Roasting pan
1-quart sauce pan
Large bowl

1 1/2 pounds Pork tenderloin
2 tablespoons Vegetable oil
1 cup Jasmine rice
6 Green onions, sliced
1 package, 6 ounces, Frozen snow peas, defrosted
1 cup Baby carrots, chopped
2 tablespoons Sesame oil
3 tablespoons Chili oil
1/2 teaspoon Salt
1/2 teaspoon Pepper
2 Limes, juiced

Ideas for Making a Balanced Meal:

Serve with a crusty roll and chilled watermelon

or

Serve with fresh pineapple and rainbow sherbet

1. Preheat oven to 425°. Rub olive oil on tenderloin and roast in the oven for 20-30 minutes, or until a meat thermometer reads 160°.

2. Cook rice according to package directions. Transfer cooked rice to a large mixing bowl.

3. Cut cooked pork into 1-inch pieces and add to rice mixture.

4. Add green onions, snow peas, carrots, sesame oil, chili oil, salt, pepper and lime juice, and stir to combine.

Serves: 6

🍏 *Recipe Nutrition per serving:*

351 calories; 23 gm protein; 18 gm carbohydrates; 20 gm total fat; **3 gm saturated fat**; 60 mg cholesterol; 2 gm fiber; **261 mg sodium**.

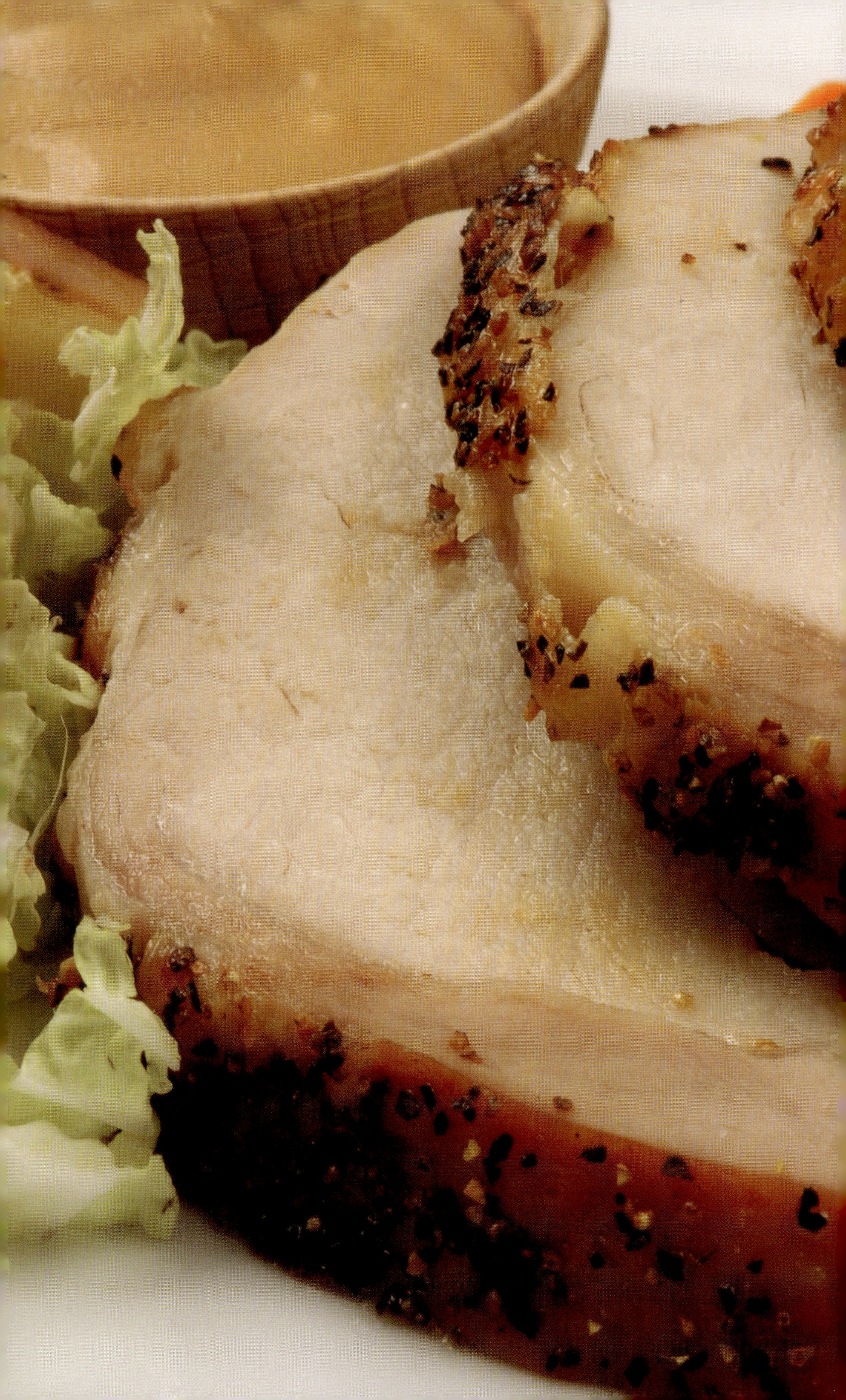

Pork Roast with Peanut Sauce

Use leftover pork in a tossed green salad for lunch the next day.

Equipment Needed:

*Roasting pan
1-quart pot*

3 pounds Boneless center cut loin, rolled and tied
3/4 teaspoon Salt
1 1/2 teaspoon Pepper
1 tablespoon Ginger, minced
1/2 cup Celery, minced
1/2 cup Onion, minced
1/2 cup Carrots, minced

Peanut Sauce:
1/2 tablespoon Vegetable oil
1 clove Garlic, minced
1/2 teaspoon Cayenne pepper
1 tablespoon Cider vinegar
1 tablespoon Reduced-sodium soy sauce
2 cups Reduced-sodium chicken broth
1/2 teaspoon Salt
1/2 cup + 1 tablespoon Peanut butter
2 tablespoons Cornstarch
1/2 cup Water

Ideas for Making a Balanced Meal:

Serve with thin spaghetti and steamed spinach

or

Serve with green peas and stewed tomatoes

1. Preheat oven to 450°. Line a roasting pan with aluminum foil.

2. Sprinkle salt, pepper and ginger over pork.

3. Place celery, onions and carrots in the bottom of the roasting pan. Place the pork, fat side up, on top of the vegetables.

4. Reduce heat to 325° and place pork in the oven. Bake for 50-55 minutes, until meat thermometer registers 160°.

5. Heat vegetable oil in a 1-quart pot over medium-high heat. Add garlic and cayenne pepper. Cook for one minute. Combine vinegar, soy sauce, chicken broth and salt in a small bowl and add to the garlic. Stir in the peanut butter until blended.

6. Whisk together the cornstarch and water in a small bowl. Whisk mixture into the sauce over low heat and bring to a simmer, stirring frequently.

7. Serve sauce with pork.

Serves: 12

Recipe Nutrition per serving:

297 calories; 26 gm protein; 8 gm carbohydrates; 18 gm total fat; 6 gm saturated fat; 68 mg cholesterol; 1 gm fiber; 505 mg sodium.

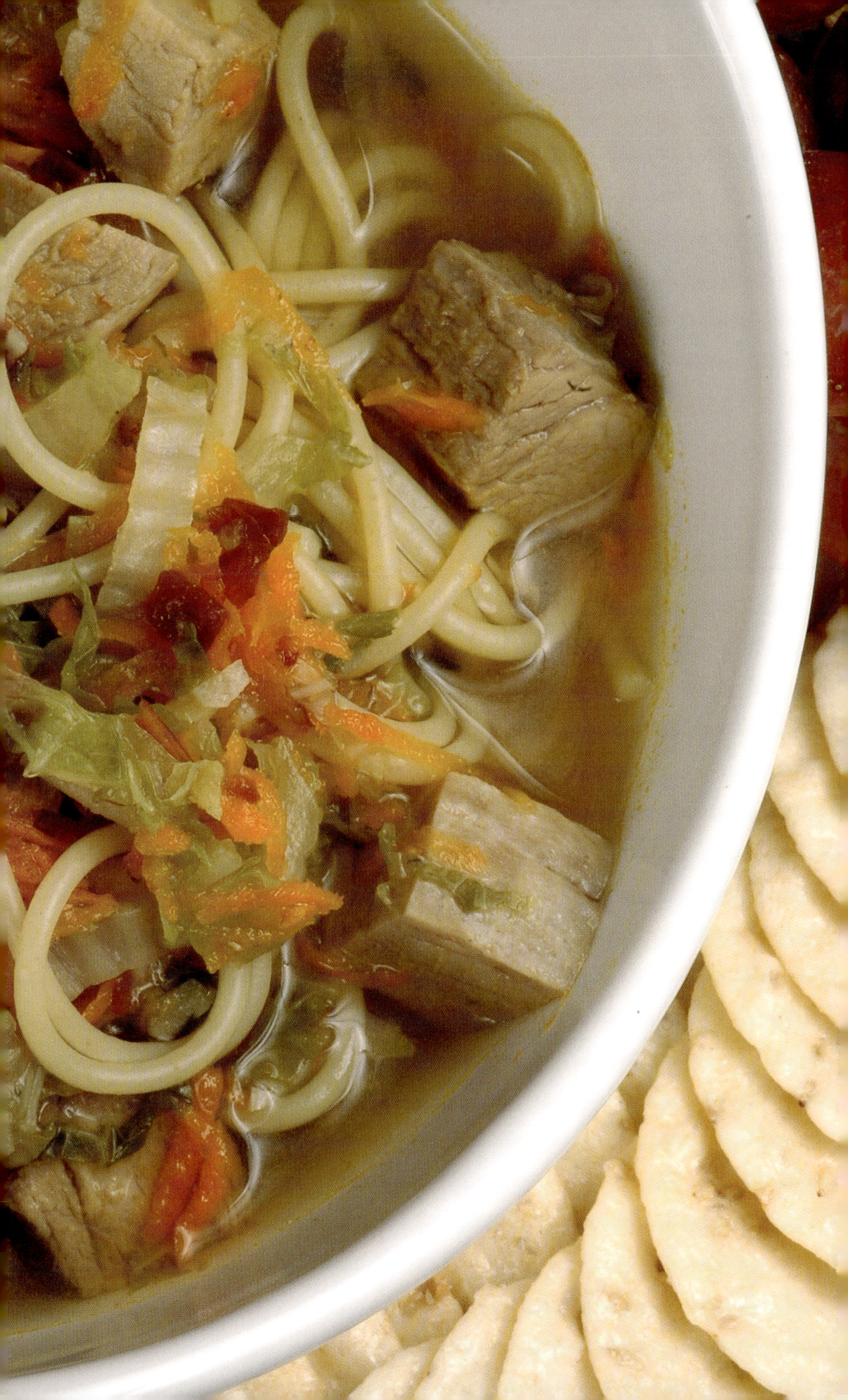

ASIAN PORK NOODLE SOUP

It's fun to use chopsticks with this flavorful, one-dish meal.

Equipment Needed:

6-quart pot

- 1/2 pound Thin spaghetti
- 2 tablespoons Vegetable oil
- 1 pound Pork tenderloin, cut into 1/2 inch pieces
- 4 cups Reduced-sodium chicken broth
- 1 cup Water
- 1 1/2 cups White wine
- 1/2 cup Reduced-sodium soy sauce
- 2 cloves Garlic, minced
- 1 tablespoon Ginger, grated
- 1/2 teaspoon Red chile paste
- 1 tablespoon Sugar
- 2 tablespoons Lime juice
- 1/2 cup Carrots, shredded
- 2 cups Napa cabbage, shredded

Garnish:
- Green onions, chopped
- Cilantro, chopped

Ideas for Making a Balanced Meal:

Serve with simple rice crackers and red grapes

or

Serve with sesame green beans and raspberry sherbet

1. Cook spaghetti according to package directions.

2. Heat oil in a 6-quart pot over medium-high heat. Brown pork for about 4 minutes, until no longer pink.

3. Add broth, water, wine and soy sauce; stir well. Add garlic, ginger, chile paste, sugar and lime juice.

4. Add carrots and cabbage. Reduce heat to medium-low, cover pot and simmer for 15 minutes until cabbage is slightly tender.

5. Serve soup over hot noodles. Garnish with chopped green onions and chopped cilantro.

Serves: 6

Recipe Nutrition per serving:

341 calories; 22 gm protein; 36 gm carbohydrates; **8 gm total fat**; **1 gm saturated fat**; 40 mg cholesterol; **3 gm fiber**; 1031 mg sodium.

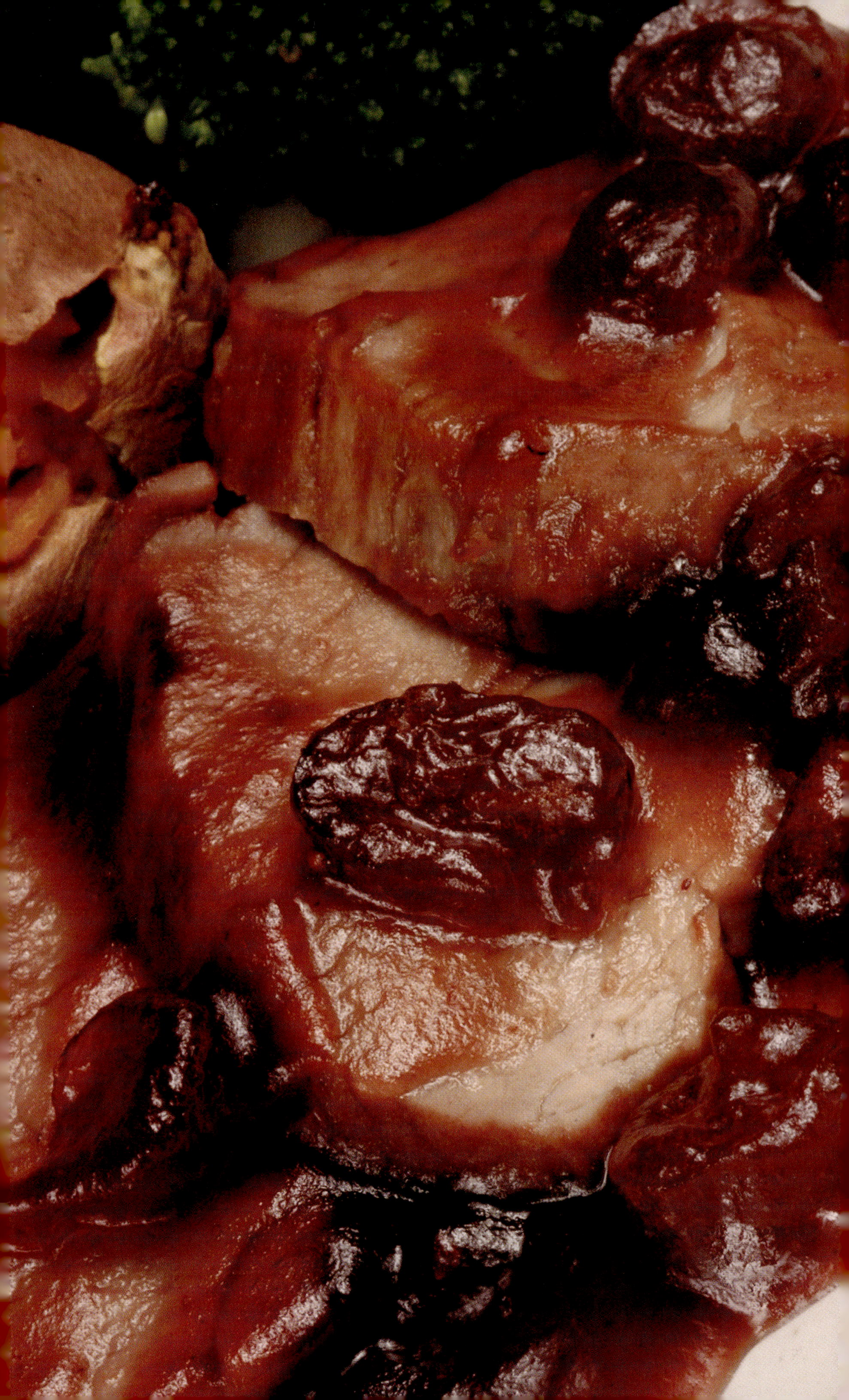

Slow-Cooked Cranberry Pork Tenderloin

This makes an easy and delicious fall meal.

Equipment Needed:

Slow-cooker or crock pot

- 2 pounds Pork tenderloin
- 1 can, 16 ounces, Jellied cranberry sauce
- 1 teaspoon Dry mustard
- 1/4 teaspoon Ground cloves
- 1 bag, 6 ounces, Dried cranberries

Ideas for Making a Balanced Meal:

Serve with a baked sweet potato and steamed broccoli

or

Serve with brown rice, steamed artichoke and a pear

1. Place pork in slow cooker.

2. In a medium bowl, mix together cranberry sauce, cranberry juice, mustard and cloves. Pour over roast. Sprinkle cranberries over roast.

3. Cook on low for 8 hours.

Serves: 8

Recipe Nutrition per serving:

269 calories; 21 gm protein; 39 gm carbohydrates; **4 gm total fat**; **1 gm saturated fat**; 60 mg cholesterol; 2 gm fiber; **60 mg sodium**.

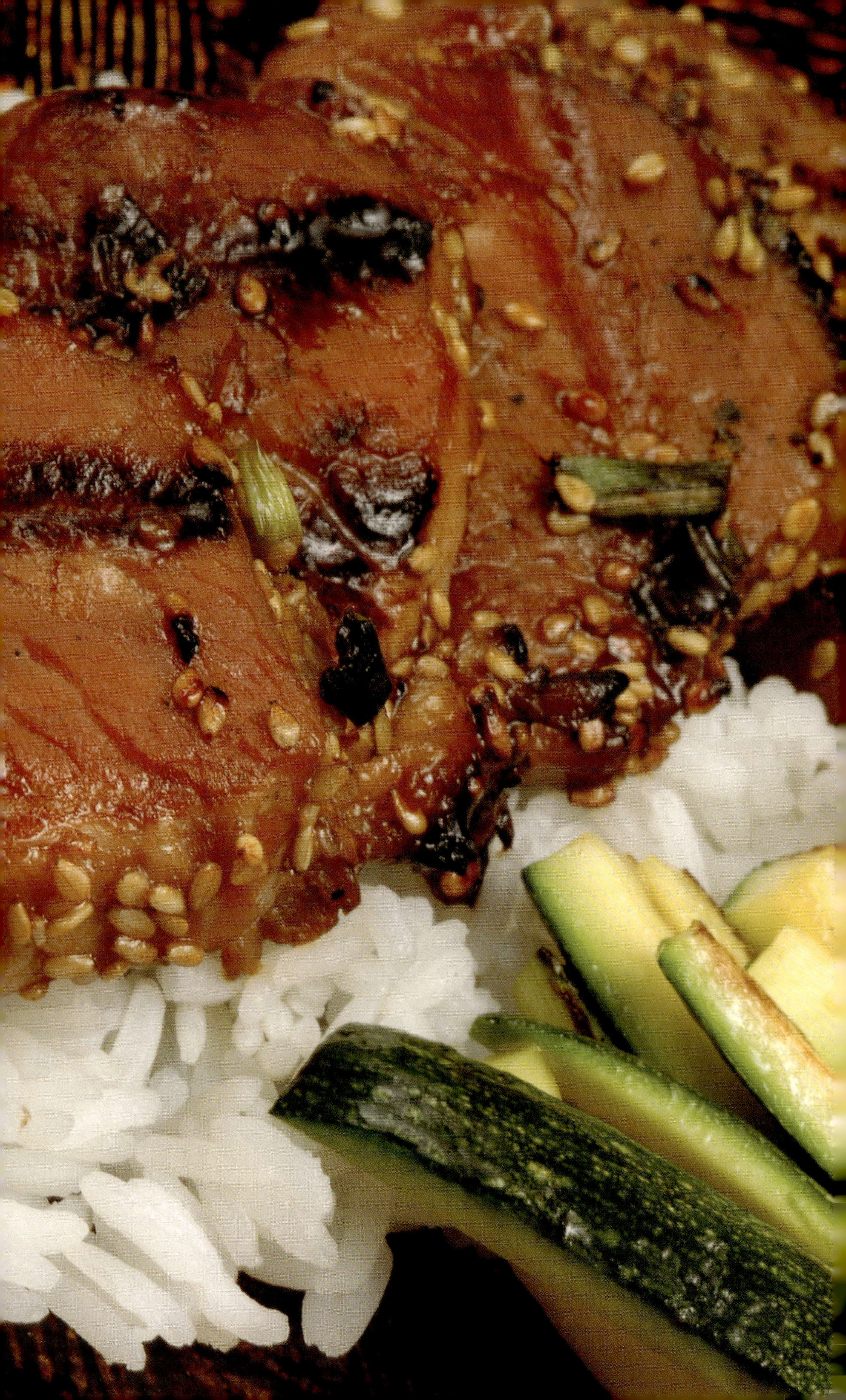

GRILLED KOREAN-STYLE PORK

Make this recipe into a Korean lettuce wrap using leaf lettuce, grilled pork and Asian pear slices.

Equipment Needed:

Grill
Blender

1/3 cup Reduced-sodium soy sauce
4 cloves Garlic, minced
5 tablespoons Sesame seeds, toasted
1/4 cup Dark brown sugar
2 pounds Pork tenderloin, cut into 1-inch thick slices
1/4 cup Green onions, chopped

Ideas for Making a Balanced Meal:

Serve with rice, kimchee (Korean-style fermented cabbage) and orange slices

or

Serve with steamed zucchini and sliced Asian pear

1. Combine soy sauce, garlic, 2 tablespoons sesame seeds, and brown sugar in blender. Blend at high speed for 30 seconds.

2. Pour marinade over the pork and marinate in the refrigerator for 1-24 hours.

3. Remove pork from marinade and grill over high heat until well done, about 5 minutes each side.

4. Serve with remaining toasted sesame seeds and green onions sprinkled on top.

Serves: 6

🍏 Recipe Nutrition per serving:

206 calories; 30 gm protein; 7 gm carbohydrates; **6 gm total fat**; **2 gm saturated fat**; 79 mg cholesterol; 1 gm fiber; **331 mg sodium**.

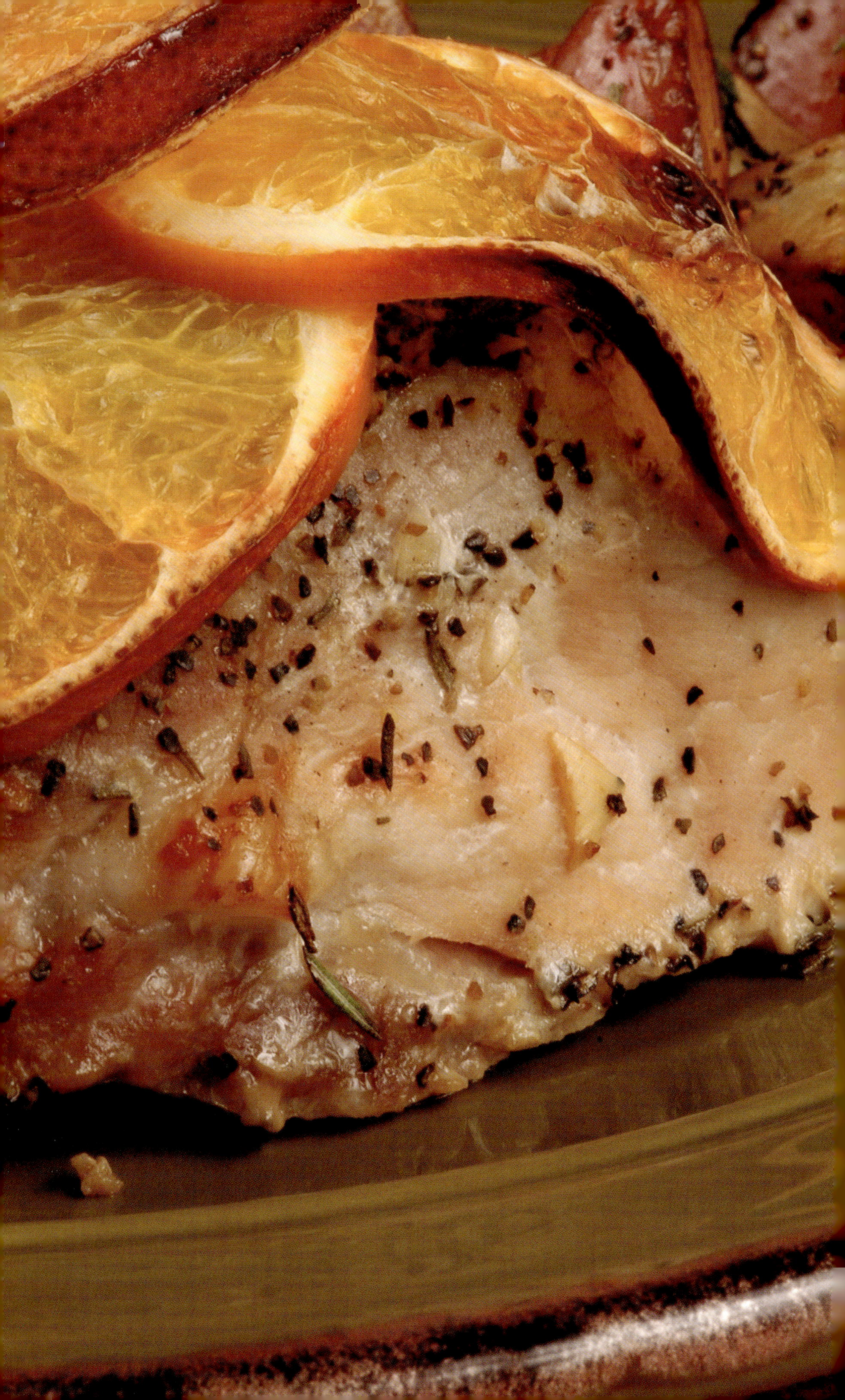

ORANGE-HONEY MARINATED PORK ROAST

You'll love the sweet, delicate flavors of this dish.

Equipment Needed:

Roasting pan

Ideas for Making a Balanced Meal:

Serve with oven roasted rosemary potatoes, green beans and sherbet

or

Serve warm, sliced on a crusty roll with horseradish and 3-bean salad

Marinade:

Juice and zest of 1 orange
1/4 cup Honey
1 cup White wine
1/2 cup Water
1 Cinnamon stick
3 Whole cloves
2 cloves Garlic, minced
1/4 cup Olive oil
1/2 tablespoon Rosemary
1/2 teaspoon Salt
1/2 teaspoon Pepper

4 pounds Boneless center cut loin roast, rolled and tied
1 small Orange, thinly sliced

1. In a zip-top bag, combine all of the marinade ingredients.

2. Place the pork in the marinade, and seal the bag. Let marinate for 1-24 hours, turning occasionally.

3. Preheat oven to 450°. Line a roasting pan with aluminum foil.

4. Remove the meat from the marinade. Place it in the roasting pan and pour the marinade over it. Place fresh orange slices on top of the pork's surface.

5. Reduce heat to 325° and place pork in oven.

6. Bake for 60-70 minutes or until meat thermometer registers 160°. Baste roast with the juice in the pan throughout the cooking time.

Serves: 16

Recipe Nutrition per serving:

232 calories; 22 gm protein; 3 gm carbohydrates; 13 gm total fat; 5 gm saturated fat; 68 mg cholesterol; 0 gm fiber; **90 mg sodium**.

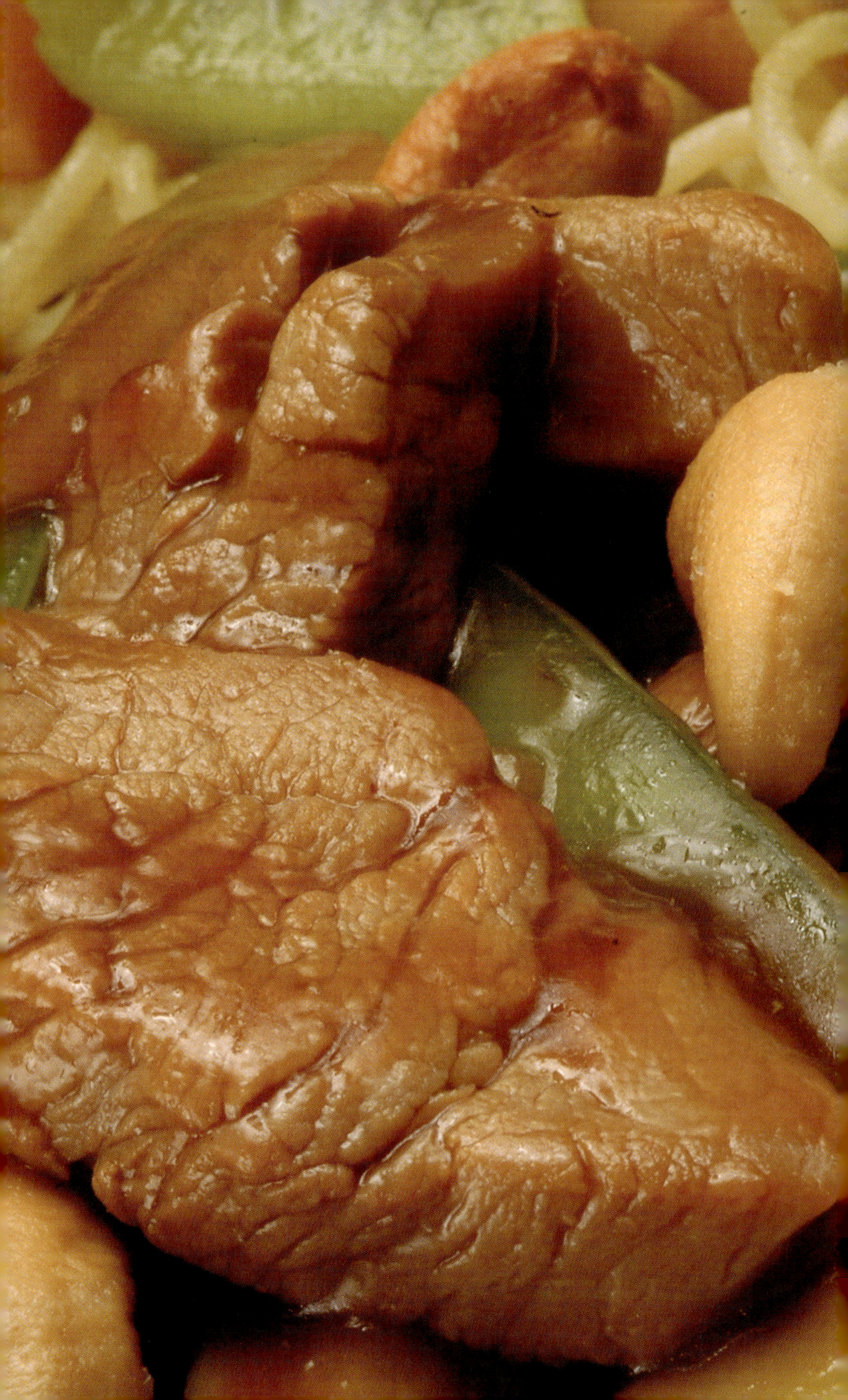

Pork Chow Mein

Try this recipe for a healthier version of Chinese takeout.

Equipment Needed:

12-inch skillet
3-quart saucepan

1/2 pound Thin spaghetti
12 ounces Pork tenderloin, cut into 1/2 inch strips
2 teaspoons Cornstarch
2 tablespoons Reduced-sodium soy sauce
1 tablespoon Sherry

1 tablespoon Vegetable oil
4 ounces Snow peas
1/2 Peeled cucumber, cut into 1/2 inch strips
1/4 cup Green onions, chopped
2 tablespoons Roasted cashews

Ideas for Making a Balanced Meal:

Serve with steamed sliced carrots and a tropical salad of kiwi, papaya and banana

or

Serve with steamed green cabbage and a chilled salad of orange and grapefruit slices

1. Break spaghetti in half. Cook according to package directions.

2. In a medium bowl, mix pork strips, corn starch, 2 teaspoons soy sauce and sherry. Allow to marinate for 10 minutes in refrigerator.

3. Heat oil in skillet. Add pork, snow peas and cucumber strips. Stir fry for 5 minutes. Add remaining soy sauce.

4. Place pork-vegetable mixture over spaghetti. Sprinkle with green onions and cashews.

Serves: 4

Recipe Nutrition per serving:

371 calories; 25 gm protein; 46 gm carbohydrates; **9 gm total fat**; **2 gm saturated fat**; 45 mg cholesterol; **4 gm fiber**; 367 mg sodium.

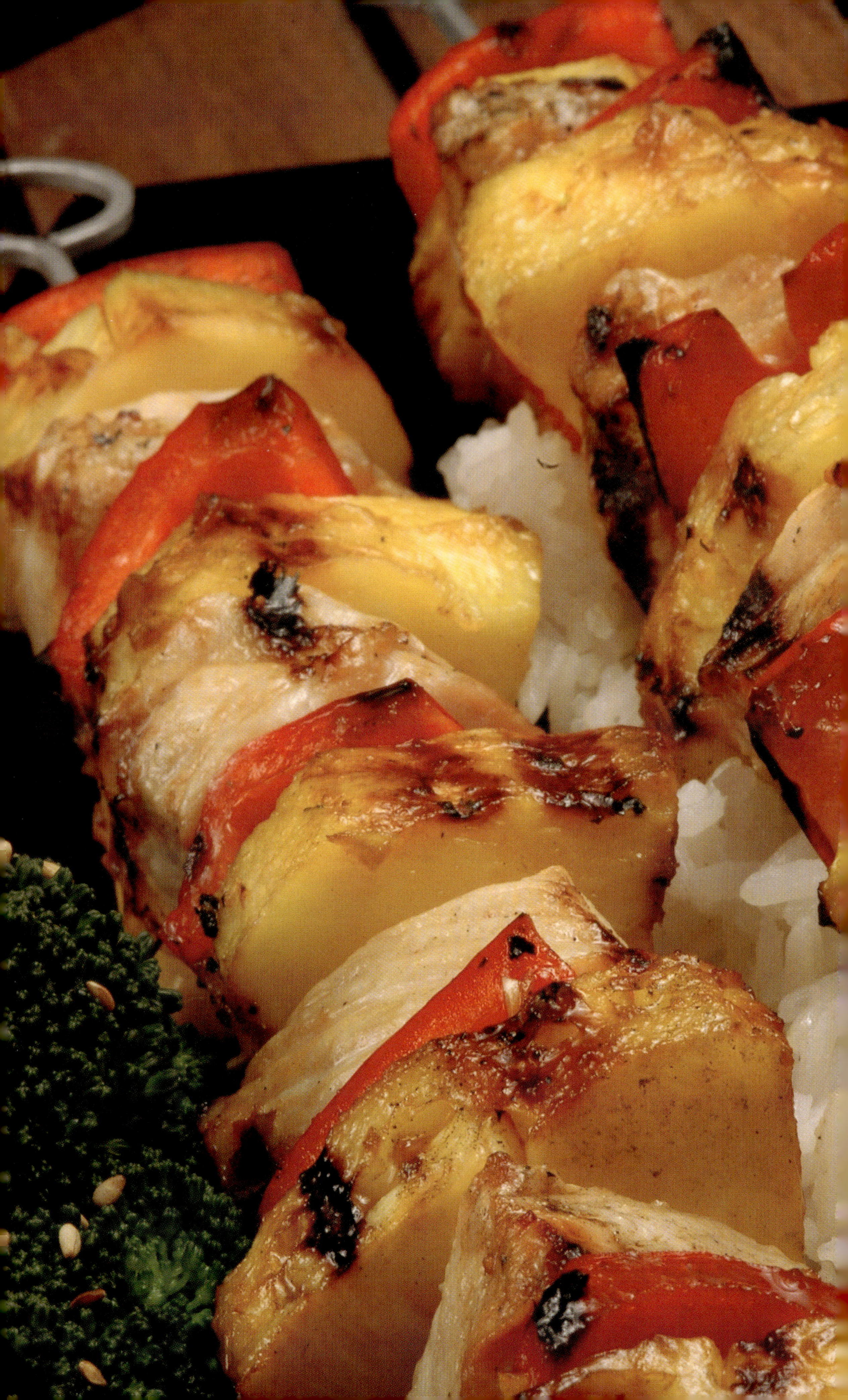

Pork and Pineapple Kabobs

This colorful recipe is a feast for the palate and for the eyes.

Equipment Needed:

Grill
Roasting pan
Small saucepan

1 pound Boneless center cut loin, cut in 1-inch cubes
1 Fresh pineapple, cut in 1-inch cubes
1 large Red bell pepper, cut in 1-inch pieces
1/2 cup Reduced-sodium soy sauce
1 teaspoon Onion powder

3 tablespoons Vegetable oil
2 tablespoons Rice vinegar
2 tablespoons Honey
2 cloves Garlic, minced
2 teaspoons Ginger, minced

Garnishes:
Green onions, sliced
Cilantro, chopped

Ideas for Making a Balanced Meal:

Serve over rice with steamed broccoli sprinkled with toasted sesame seeds

or

Serve with lightly sautéed spinach, crusty bread and rainbow sherbet

1. Preheat grill to medium heat.

2. Alternately thread pieces of pineapple, pork and red pepper onto metal skewers.

3. In a small bowl, combine soy sauce, onion powder, oil, vinegar, honey, garlic and ginger.

4. Place skewers in a roasting pan and pour marinade over them. Turn to coat. Place in refrigerator and marinate for 1-24 hours, turning occasionally.

5. Remove kabobs from marinade; reserve marinade.

6. Grill kabobs over medium heat, turning occasionally, about 20 minutes, until internal temperature reaches 160°.

7. Bring marinade to a boil and boil for 2 minutes.

8. Sprinkle kabobs with green onions and cilantro and serve with marinade.

Serves: 4

Recipe Nutrition per serving:

346 calories; 25 gm protein; 25 gm carbohydrates; 17 gm fat; 5 gm saturated fat; 68 mg cholesterol; **3 gm fiber**; 658 mg sodium.

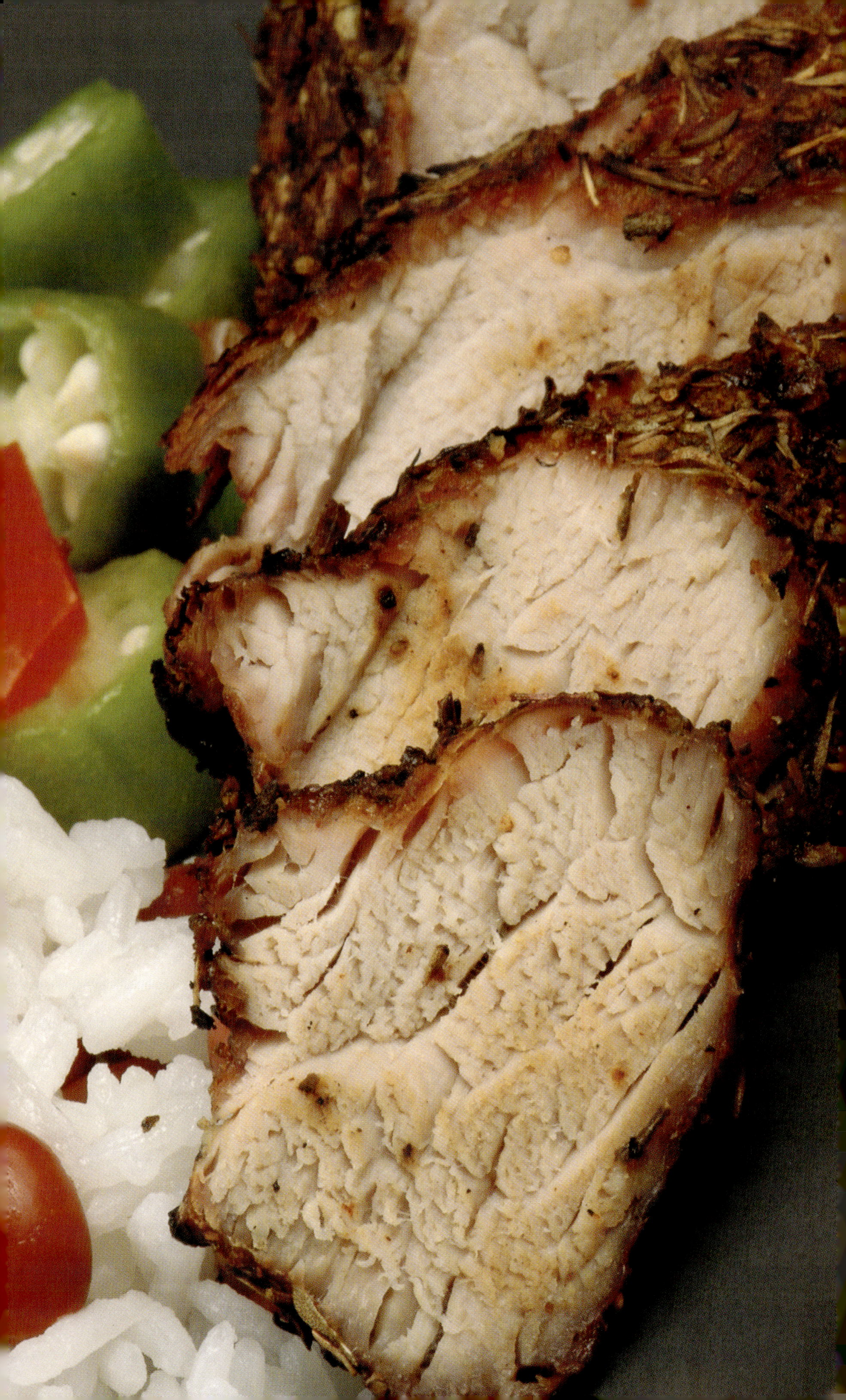

Pork Tenderloin with Cajun Rub

This recipe can be made as spicy or mild as you like.

Equipment Needed:

Grill

1 tablespoon Ground paprika
1/2 teaspoon Salt
1 teaspoon Onion powder
1 teaspoon Garlic powder
1/2 teaspoon Cayenne pepper
1/2 teaspoon Pepper
1/2 teaspoon Dried thyme
1/2 teaspoon Dried oregano
1 pound Pork tenderloin

Ideas for Making a Balanced Meal:

Serve with red beans and rice, steamed okra, and a fresh fruit salad

or

Serve with baked sweet potato, French style green beans and a slice of melon

1. Mix together the paprika, salt, onion powder, garlic powder, cayenne pepper, pepper, thyme and oregano in a small bowl.

2. Rub the Cajun mixture onto all outside surfaces of the pork.

3. Wrap the pork in plastic wrap and place it in the refrigerator.

4. Allow the flavors to develop for 1-24 hours.

5. Unwrap the pork and grill it over high heat for about 5 minutes per side, depending on the thickness. The pork is done when a meat thermometer reads 160°.

Serves: 4

Recipe Nutrition per serving:

132 calories; 22 gm protein; 2 gm carbohydrates; **3 gm total fat**;
1 gm saturated fat; 60 mg cholesterol; 1 gm fiber; **340 mg sodium**.

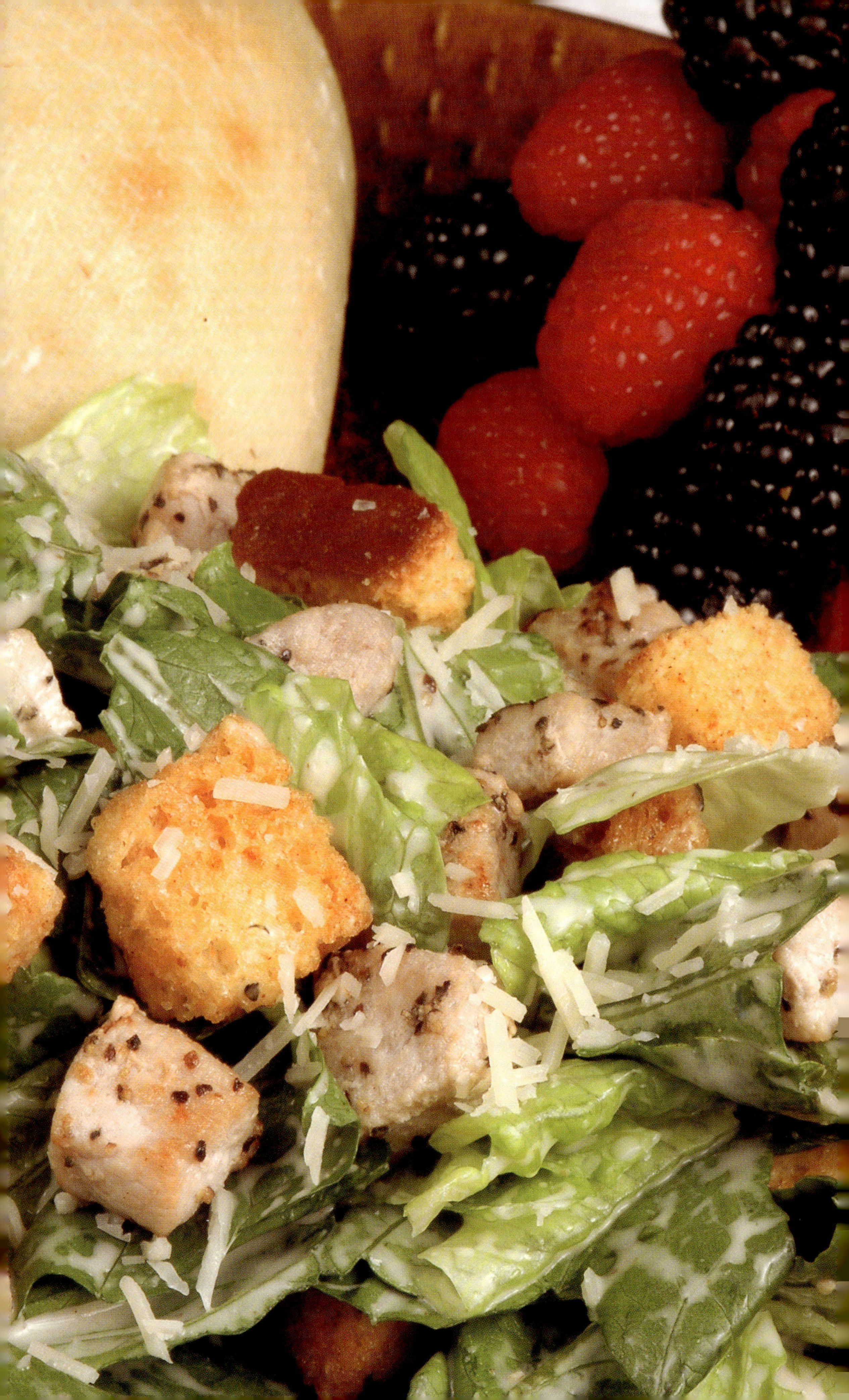

EASY CAESAR PORK SALAD

This entrée salad is quick, easy and satisfying.

Equipment Needed:

12-inch skillet

Large bowl

1 tablespoon Vegetable oil
1 pound Boneless pork loin, cut into bite-size cubes
2 heads Romaine lettuce, rinsed and dried
1/2 cup Light bottled caesar salad dressing
1 Lemon or lime, juiced
1/4 cup Parmesan cheese, shredded or grated
1/4 cup Croutons

Ideas for Making a Balanced Meal:

Serve with fresh bread and chilled blueberries

or

Serve with warmed corn tortillas and sliced mango

1. Pour vegetable oil into a 12-inch skillet and heat over medium-high heat. Add the pork to heated skillet and cook while stirring for 6-8 minutes. When the pork cubes are brown on all sides remove them from skillet.

2. Tear lettuce into bite-size pieces and place into a large bowl.

3. Mix salad dressing with lemon or lime juice and drizzle onto lettuce.

4. Toss lettuce to distribute dressing evenly.

5. Divide lettuce into 4 serving plates or bowls. Top with pork.

6. Sprinkle Parmesan cheese on each salad and top with croutons.

Serves: 4

Recipe Nutrition per serving:

325 calories; 26 gm protein; 7 gm carbohydrates; 21 gm total fat; 6 gm saturated fat; 78 mg cholesterol; 2 gm fiber; **276 mg sodium**.

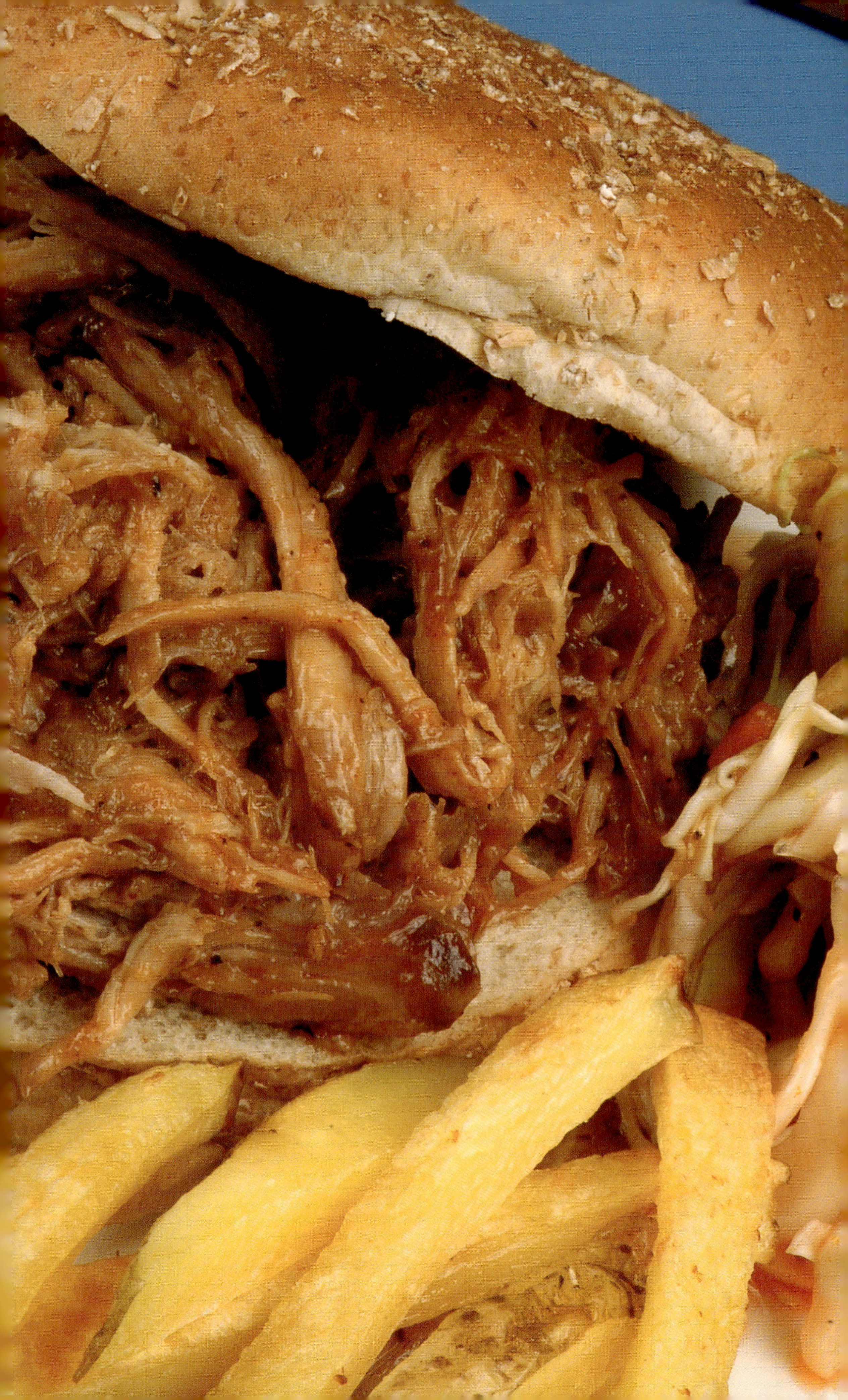

LEXINGTON STYLE PORK BBQ SANDWICH

For an easier version, use bottled sauce instead of making your own.

Equipment Needed:

Grill

4 pounds Boston butt roast

Sauce:
1 1/2 cups Cider vinegar
1/2 cup Ketchup
1/2 cup Water
1 teaspoon Salt
1/2 teaspoon Cayenne pepper
1/8 teaspoon Red pepper flakes
1 tablespoon Sugar
16 Hamburger buns

BBQ Slaw:
1 large Head cabbage, shredded
3/4 cup Ketchup
1/4 teasoon Salt
1/2 cup Sugar
1/3 cup Vinegar
1 teaspoon Pepper
Dash of Cayenne pepper

Ideas for Making a Balanced Meal:

Serve with pasta salad and fresh mixed fruit

or

Serve with baked French fries, carrot sticks and an orange

1. Heat grill. Place meat on grill rack over indirect heat and cook for 4-5 hours or until meat falls apart.

2. Mix all sauce ingredients together while pork is cooking.

3. Remove meat from grill, shred and mix with sauce.

4. Combine BBQ slaw ingredients. Chill before serving.

5. Make each sandwich with one bun, 4 ounces pork and about 1/4 cup coleslaw.

Serves: 16

Recipe Nutrition per serving:
369 calories; 20 gm protein; 38 gm carbohydrates; 14 gm total fat; 5 gm saturated fat; 56 mg cholesterol; **3 gm fiber**; 657 mg sodium.

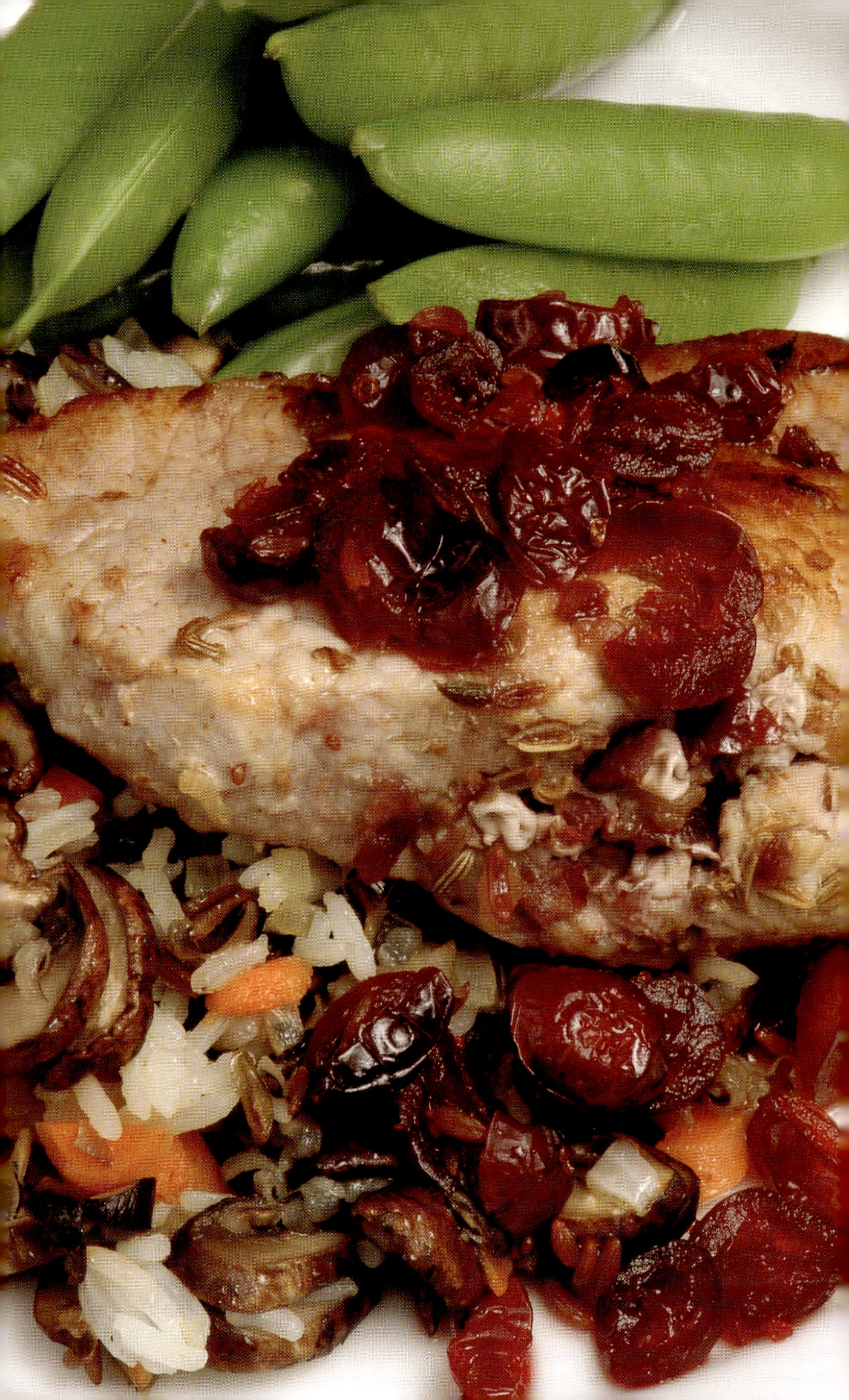

Cranberry-Walnut Stuffed Pork Chops

This recipe is perfect for a nice holiday meal.

Equipment Needed:

Oven-proof skillet

4 Loin chops, thick sliced
2 tablespoons Walnuts, chopped
2 tablespoons Dried cranberries
1 teaspoon Fennel seeds

Sauce:
3 tablespoons Butter
3/4 cup Dried cranberries
1/2 cup Red wine
1/2 teaspoon Fennel seeds
1/2 cup Reduced-sodium chicken broth

Ideas for Making a Balanced Meal:

Serve with wild rice pilaf and sugar snap peas

or

Serve with mashed potatoes and steamed Brussels sprouts

1. Preheat oven to 325º.

2. Combine walnuts, cranberries and fennel seeds in a small bowl.

3. Cut a 2-3 inch slit in the side of each pork chop to form a pocket.

4. Place 1 1/2 tablespoons of the mixture into the pocket of each chop.

5. Heat an ovenproof skillet to medium-high heat. Add chops; cook 3 minutes per side. Cover skillet with lid or aluminum foil and place it in the preheated oven. Cook chops about 10 minutes, until the internal temperature reaches 160º.

6. Remove skillet from oven and remove chops from skillet.

7. Place skillet on stove on medium heat. Add sauce ingredients, bring to a simmer and cook until sauce thickens.

8. Serve sauce over chops.

Serves: 4

Recipe Nutrition per serving:

405 calories; 25 gm protein; 24 gm carbohydrates; 22 gm total fat; 9 gm saturated fat; 101 mg cholesterol; 2 gm fiber; **184 mg sodium**.

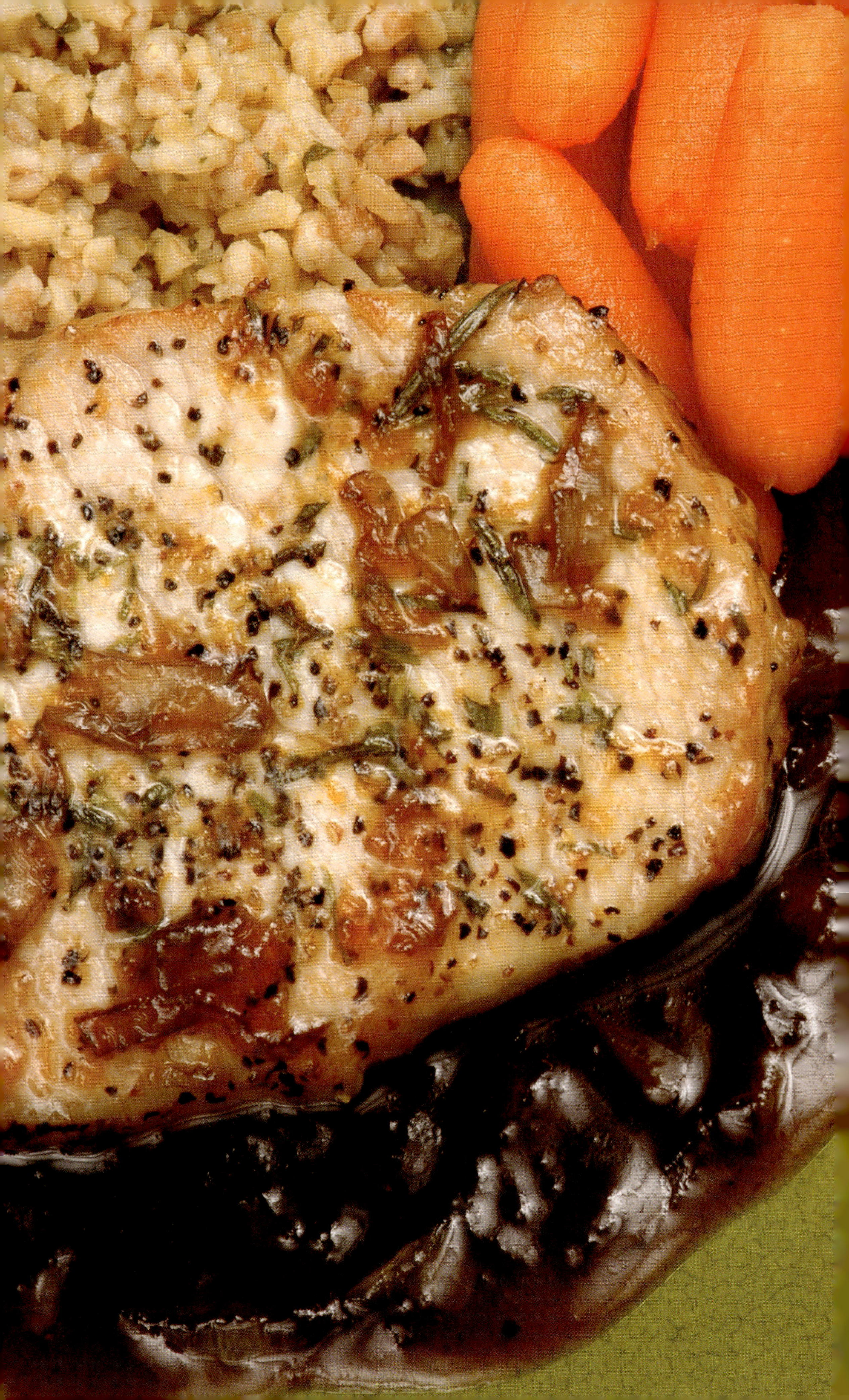

Pork Chops with Apricot Onion Marmalade

Feel free to use your favorite jam in this recipe.

Equipment Needed:

12-inch skillet

1 pound Boneless center cut loin chops
1 teaspoon Rosemary, minced
1/2 teaspoon Salt
1/2 teaspoon Pepper

2 tablespoons Vegetable oil
1 large Onion, thinly sliced
1/2 cup Water
1/4 cup Balsamic vinegar
1/4 cup Apricot jam

Ideas for Making a Balanced Meal:

Serve with whole wheat couscous and broccoli slaw

or

Serve with boiled red skinned potatoes and steamed baby carrots

1. Sprinkle both sides of pork chops with rosemary, salt and pepper.

2. Heat oil in a 12-inch skillet over medium-high heat.

3. Place chops in skillet and cook for one minute on each side, until lightly browned.

4. Remove chops from pan onto a plate.

5. Add onion to skillet and cook on medium-high heat until translucent, about 5 minutes.

6. Add water, vinegar and jam. Bring to a boil, reduce heat, cover and simmer on medium-low heat until onions are very tender, about 20-25 minutes.

7. Return pork to skillet, placing on top of the onions and cover pan. Cook over medium heat for 6-8 minutes, until most of the liquid has evaporated, and pork has cooked through.

Serves: 4

Recipe Nutrition per serving:

377 calories; 30 gm protein; 19 gm carbohydrates; 20 gm total fat; 5 gm saturated fat; 95 mg cholesterol; 1 gm fiber; 366 mg sodium.

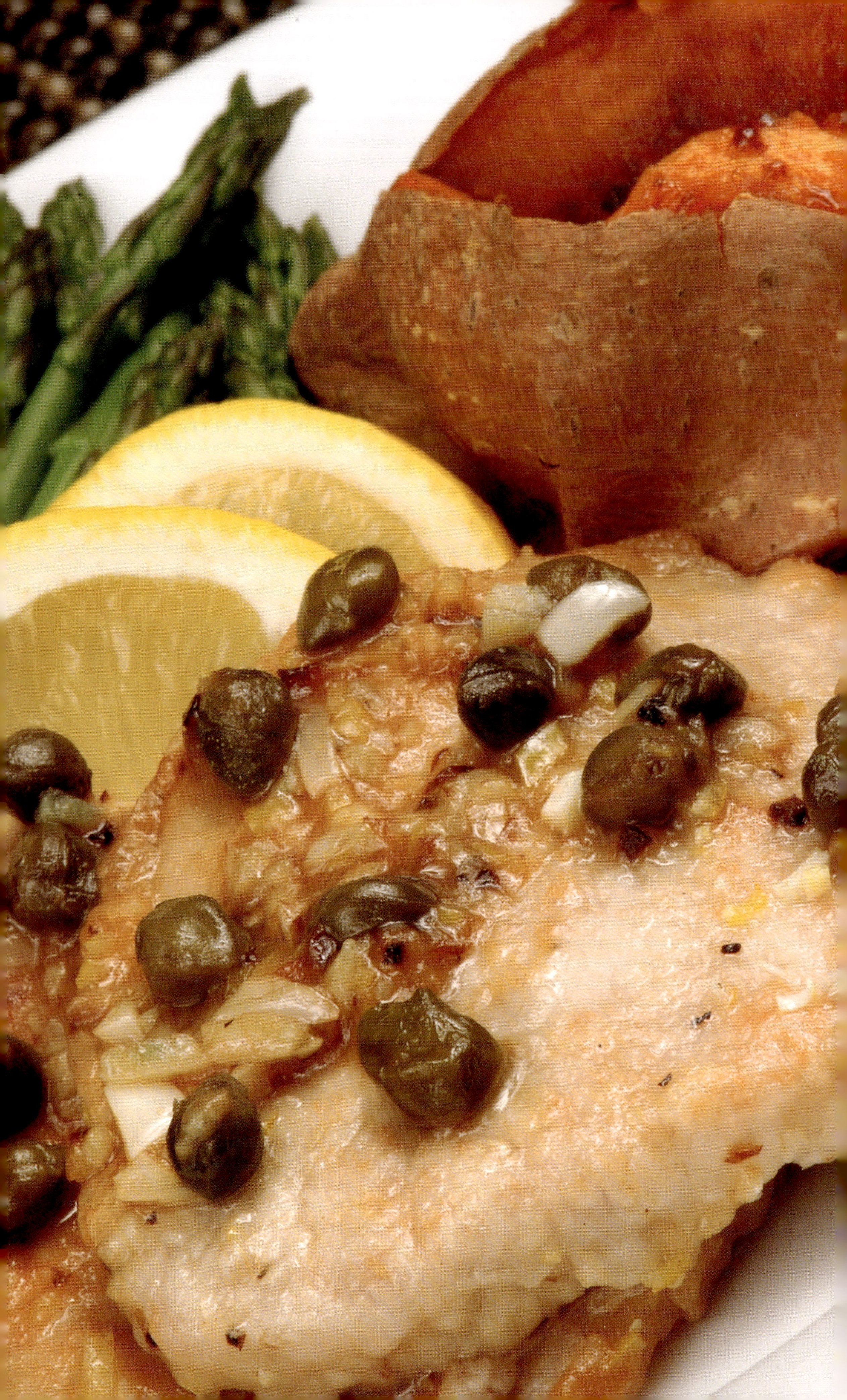

PORK PICCATA

Lemons give this classic pork dish a fresh flavor.

Equipment Needed:

12-inch skillet

1 pound Boneless center cut loin chops, thin sliced
1/2 teaspoon Salt
1/2 teaspoon Pepper
1/3 cup All-purpose flour
1 tablespoon Olive oil

2 cloves Garlic, minced
1/4 cup Lemon juice
1/2 teaspoon Lemon zest, grated
1/2 cup Dry white wine
1/2 cup Chicken broth
1/4 cup Capers, drained

Ideas for Making a Balanced Meal:

Serve with a baked sweet potato and steamed Italian green beans

or

Serve with lightly buttered grits and a salad of sliced tomatoes and arugula

1. Combine salt, pepper and flour in a shallow dish.

2. Add pork to flour mixture and coat both sides, shaking off excess flour.

3. Heat oil in a 12-inch skillet over medium-heat. Add pork and sauté 2 minutes per side, until golden brown.

4. Add garlic, lemon juice, lemon zest, wine and broth. Simmer for 5-6 minutes, until pork is cooked through and half of the sauce has evaporated.

5. Add capers. Simmer 1 minute to heat through.

Serves: 4

Recipe Nutrition per serving:

310 calories; 31 gm protein; 11 gm carbohydrates; 13 gm total fat; 4 gm saturated fat; 95 mg cholesterol; 1 gm fiber; 680 mg sodium.

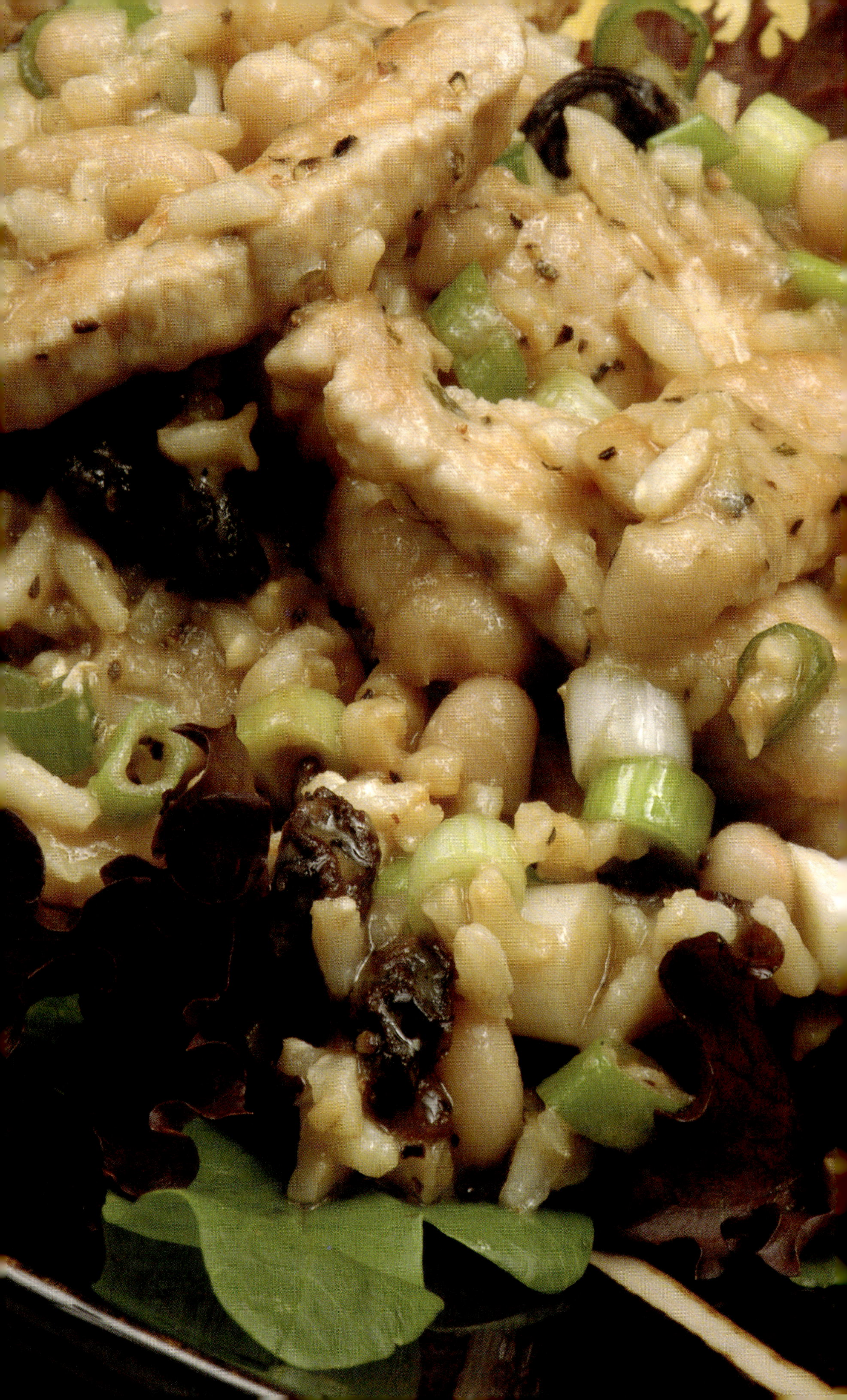

PORK AND BEAN SALAD

Substitute any dried fruit for the raisins in this recipe.

Equipment Needed:

2-quart saucepan
12-inch skillet

1 package, 6 ounces, Brown and wild rice mix
1/4 cup Dijon mustard
2 tablespoons Olive oil
2 tablespoons Balsamic vinegar
1/4 teaspoon Pepper
1 1/2 pounds Boneless center cut loin chops, cut into 1/2-inch wide strips

1/2 cup Raisins
4 Green onions, sliced
1 can, 15 ounces, Navy beans, rinsed and drained
6 cups Assorted salad greens

Ideas for Making a Balanced Meal:

Serve with a tomato and cucumber salad and mixed fresh fruit

or

Serve with chilled green beans vinaigrette and breadsticks

1. Prepare rice according to package directions, omitting oil.

2. Make dressing by combining mustard, oil, vinegar and pepper in a small bowl. Set aside.

3. Heat oil in a 12-inch skillet over medium-high heat. Add pork strips and stir-fry until pork is cooked through, about 3 minutes.

4. Add pork, raisins, green onions and beans to cooked rice. Pour dressing over and mix to combine.

5. Serve on top of salad greens.

Serves: 8

Recipe Nutrition per serving:

416 calories; 30 gm protein; 42 gm carbohydrates; 15 gm total fat; 4 gm saturated fat; 71 mg cholesterol; **8 gm fiber**; **252 mg sodium**.

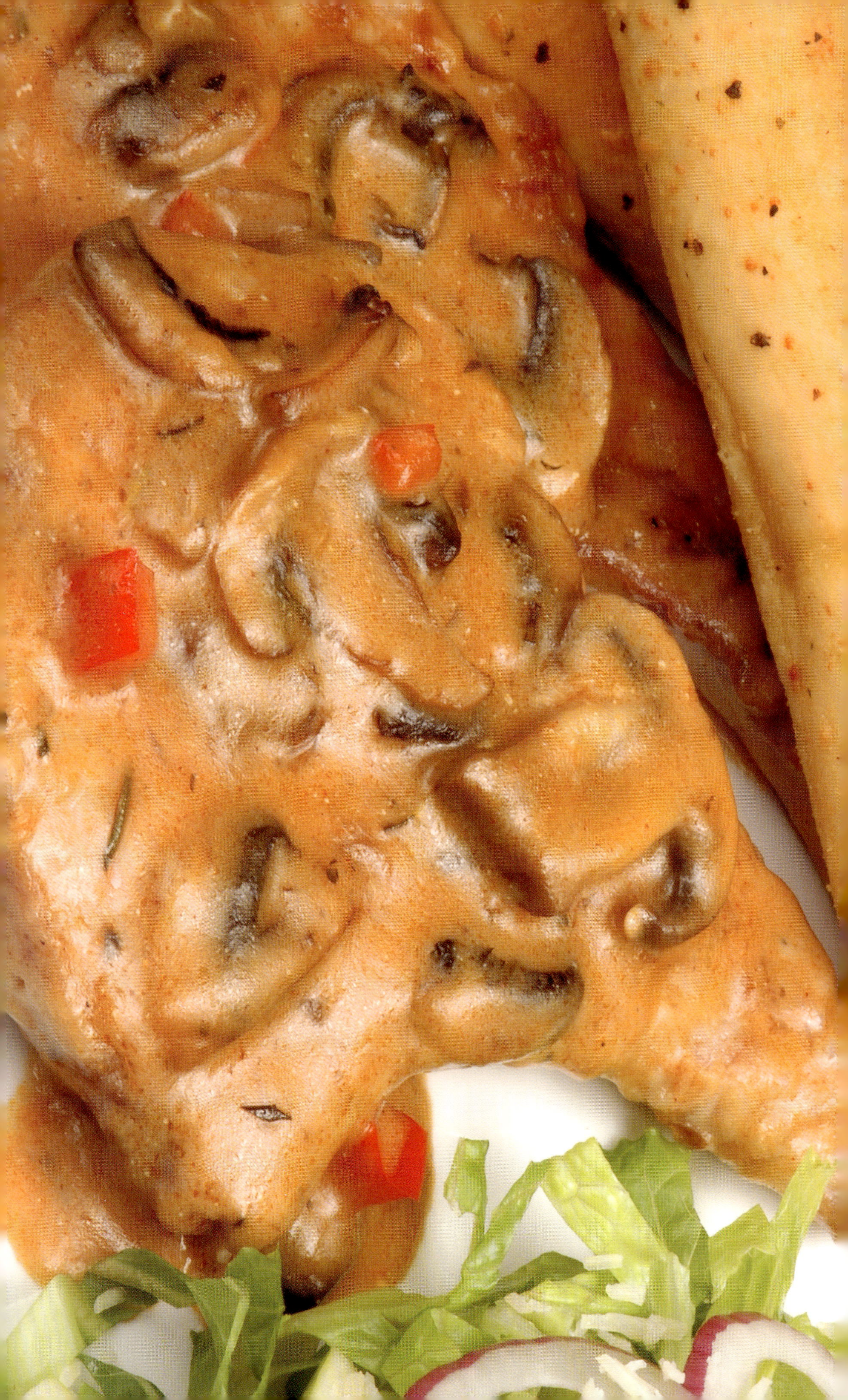

Fancy Pork Chop Casserole

Serve this recipe over white or brown rice to absorb the sauce.

Equipment Needed:

12-inch skillet
9x13 baking dish

- 3/4 cup Flour
- 1 teaspoon Salt
- 1 teaspoon Pepper
- 2 tablespoons Vegetable oil
- 1 1/2 pounds Bone-in pork chops
- 8 ounces Sliced mushrooms
- 1/2 cup Red bell pepper, chopped
- 1 can, 10 3/4 ounces, Golden mushroom soup
- 2/3 cup Chicken broth
- 1 teaspoon Garlic powder
- 1 teaspoon Dried rosemary
- 1 cup Reduced-fat sour cream
- 1 tablespoon Paprika

Ideas for Making a Balanced Meal:

Serve with steamed snow peas and a salad of Romaine lettuce, sliced apples and sliced red onions

or

Serve with breadsticks and fresh pears

1. Preheat oven to 350°.

2. In a shallow dish, combine flour, salt and pepper. Coat both sides of each pork chop with the flour mixture.

3. Heat oil in a 12-inch skillet, and brown pork chops 2-3 minutes per side.

4. Place pork chops in a 9x13 baking dish.

5. In a medium bowl, combine mushrooms, pepper, soup, broth, garlic powder, rosemary and sour cream. Pour over chops.

6. Sprinkle top with paprika. Cover with aluminum foil and bake for 45-60 minutes, until casserole is heated through.

Serves: 6

Recipe Nutrition per serving:

369 calories; 24 gm protein; 21 gm carbohydrates; 21 gm total fat; 7 gm saturated fat; 71 mg cholesterol; 2 gm fiber; 875 mg sodium.

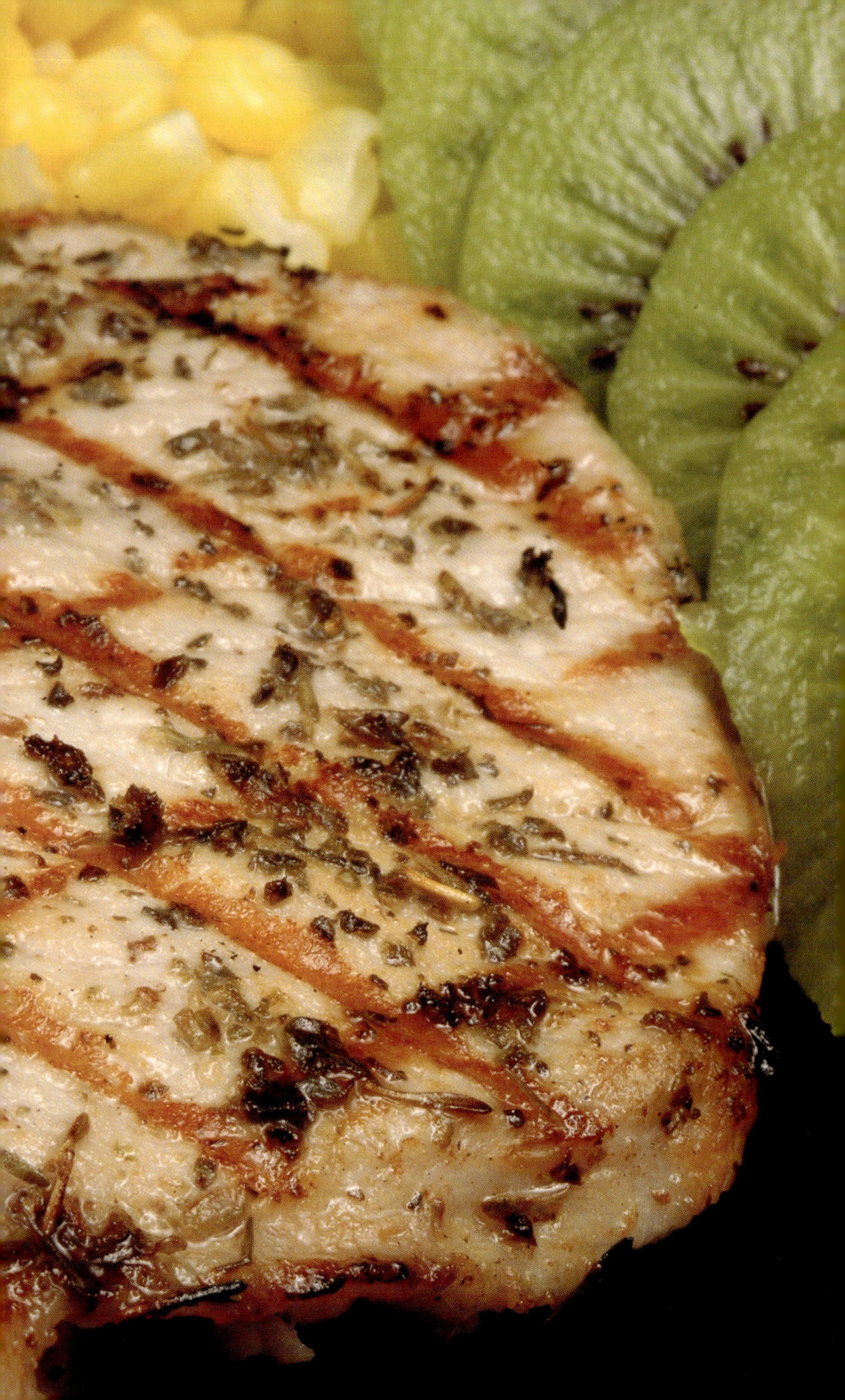

GRILLED PORK CHOPS WITH HERB RUB

This flavorful blend of herbs really dresses up a pork chop.

Equipment Needed:

Grill

1/2 tablespoon Dried or ground thyme
1/2 tablespoon Dried or ground marjoram
1/2 tablespoon Dried sage
1/2 tablespoon Dried basil
1/2 tablespoon Lemon zest
1 pound Center cut loin chops

Ideas for Making a Balanced Meal:

Serve with corn, red cabbage cole slaw and kiwi

or

Serve with noodles, sautéed broccoli and sliced red pears

1. Mix together the thyme, marjoram, sage, basil and lemon zest in a small bowl.

2. Rub the herb mixture onto all surfaces of the pork chops.

3. Wrap the pork chops in plastic wrap and place them in the refrigerator.

4. Allow the flavors to develop for 1-24 hours.

5. Unwrap the pork chops and grill them over high heat for about 5 minutes per side, depending on the thickness. The pork is done when a meat thermometer reads 160°.

Serves: 4

Recipe Nutrition per serving:

152 calories; 18 gm protein; 5 gm carbohydrates; **7 gm total fat**; **3 gm saturated fat**; 48 mg cholesterol; **3 gm fiber**; **46 mg sodium**.

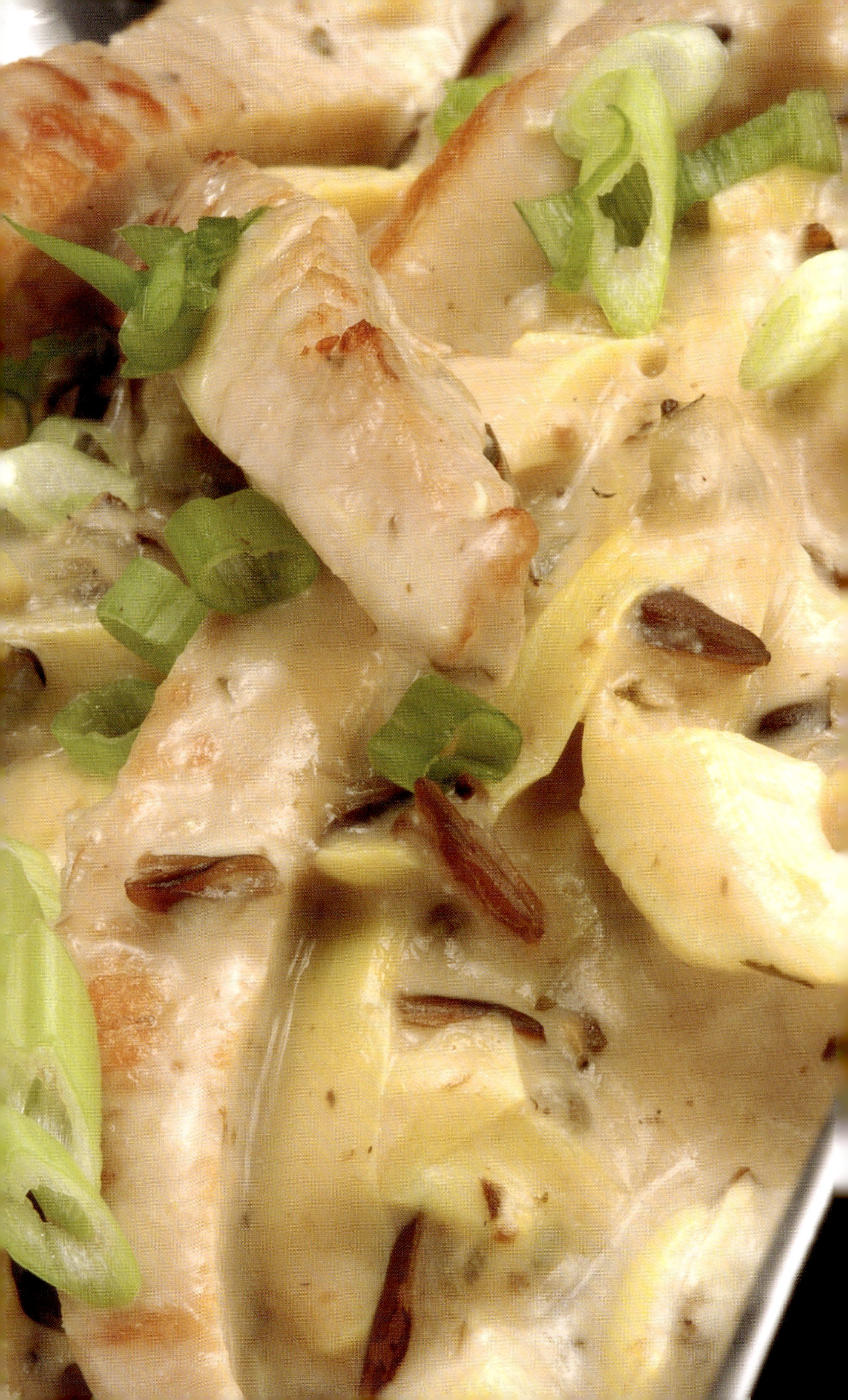

PORK AND WILD RICE CASSEROLE

For a healthier casserole, you can use vegetable oil instead of butter and reduced-fat versions of sour cream and mushroom soup.

Equipment Needed:

3-quart saucepan
9x13 baking dish

1 package, 6 ounces, Quick cooking long grain and wild rice mix
1/2 tablespoon Vegetable oil
1 pound Boneless center cut loin chops, cut into 1/2 inch strips
1 tablespoon Butter

8 ounces Mushrooms, sliced
1 can, 14.5 ounces, Artichoke hearts, drained and chopped
1/2 cup Reduced-fat sour cream
1 can, 10 3/4 ounces, Cream of mushroom soup, condensed
3 Green onions, sliced

Ideas for Making a Balanced Meal:

Serve with steamed asparagus and chilled, shredded carrots with vinaigrette dressing

or

Serve with steamed broccoli spears and a simple tossed salad with lemon juice-olive oil dressing

1. Preheat oven to 350º. Prepare rice according to package directions.

2. Heat oil in 3-quart sauce pan over medium-high heat. Sauté pork strips, stirring frequently, for about 4 minutes until no longer pink. Remove pork from pan.

3. Melt butter in sauce pan and sauté mushrooms until browned.

4. Combine pork, rice, mushrooms, artichokes, sour cream, soup and 1/2 of the green onions.

5. Pour into a 9x13 baking dish. Sprinkle remaining green onions on top.

6. Bake uncovered for 30 minutes, or until heated through.

Serves: 6

Nutrition per serving:

353 calories; 21 gm protein; 31 gm carbohydrates; 16 gm total fat; 6 gm saturated fat; 58 mg cholesterol; **4 gm fiber**; 708 mg sodium.

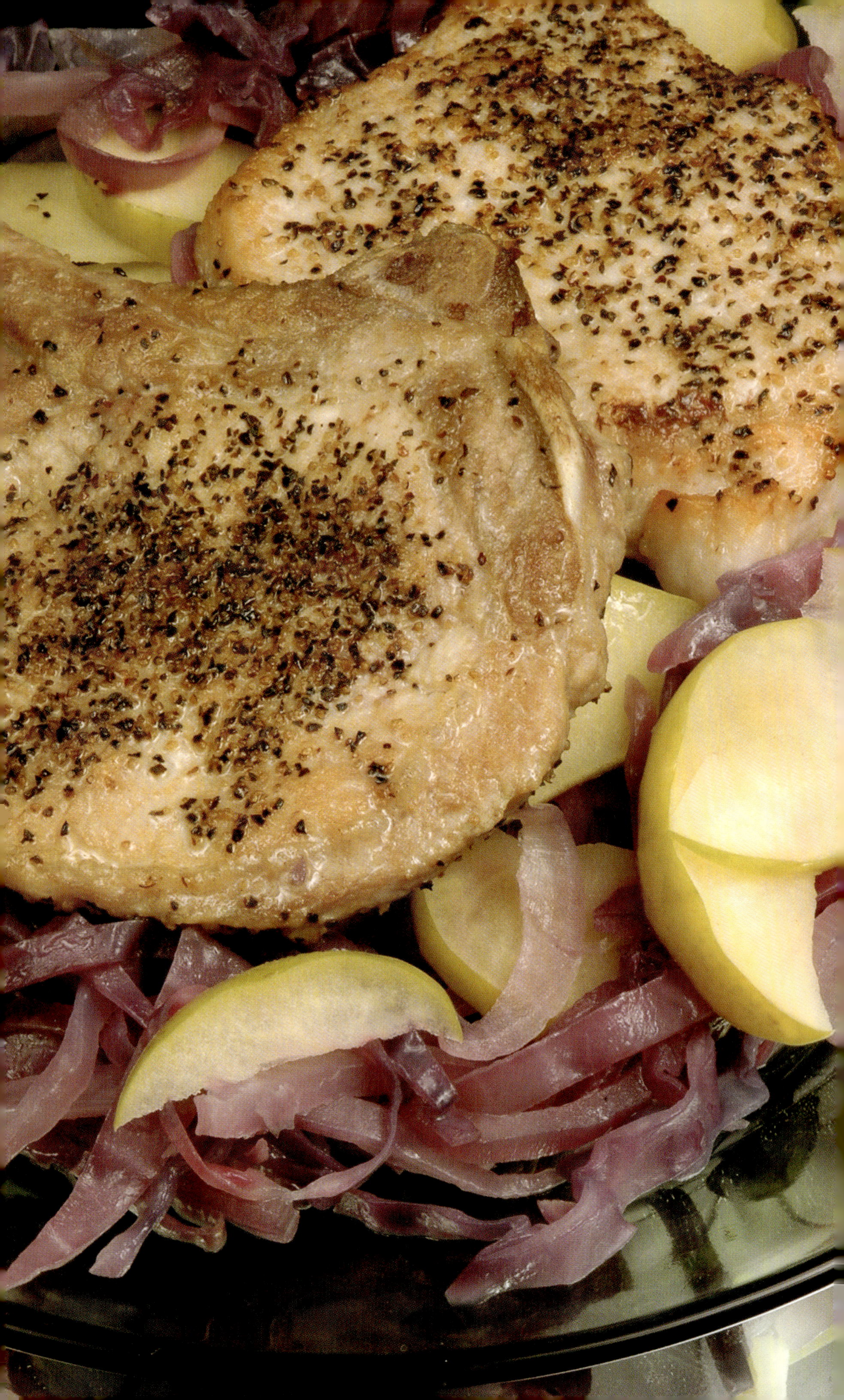

Pork Chops with Braised Red Cabbage

This is a great recipe for a cold day.

Equipment Needed:

12-inch skillet

2 pounds Bone-in center cut loin chops, 1/2 inch thick
1/2 teaspoon Salt
1/4 teaspoon Pepper
1 medium head Red cabbage, shredded
2 Granny Smith apples, thinly sliced
1 large Red onion, sliced
1/4 cup Water
1/4 cup Red wine vinegar
2 tablespoons Brown sugar, packed

Ideas for Making a Balanced Meal:

Serve with boiled potatoes and spinach-mushroom salad

or

Serve with noodles and warm cinnamon applesauce

1. Remove fat from pork chops. Sprinkle both sides of pork with salt and pepper.

2. Heat a 12-inch skillet over medium-high heat. Cook pork in skillet, turning once until brown. Cook in batches if necessary. Remove pork from skillet.

3. Mix remaining ingredients in skillet. Heat to a boil, stirring occasionally. Place pork on top; reduce heat. Cover and simmer 45 minutes or until meat thermometer reaches 160°.

Serves: 6

🍏 Recipe Nutrition per serving:

318 calories; 27 gm protein; 25 gm carbohydrates; 13 gm total fat; 5 gm saturated fat; 72 mg cholesterol; **5 gm fiber**; **278 mg sodium**.

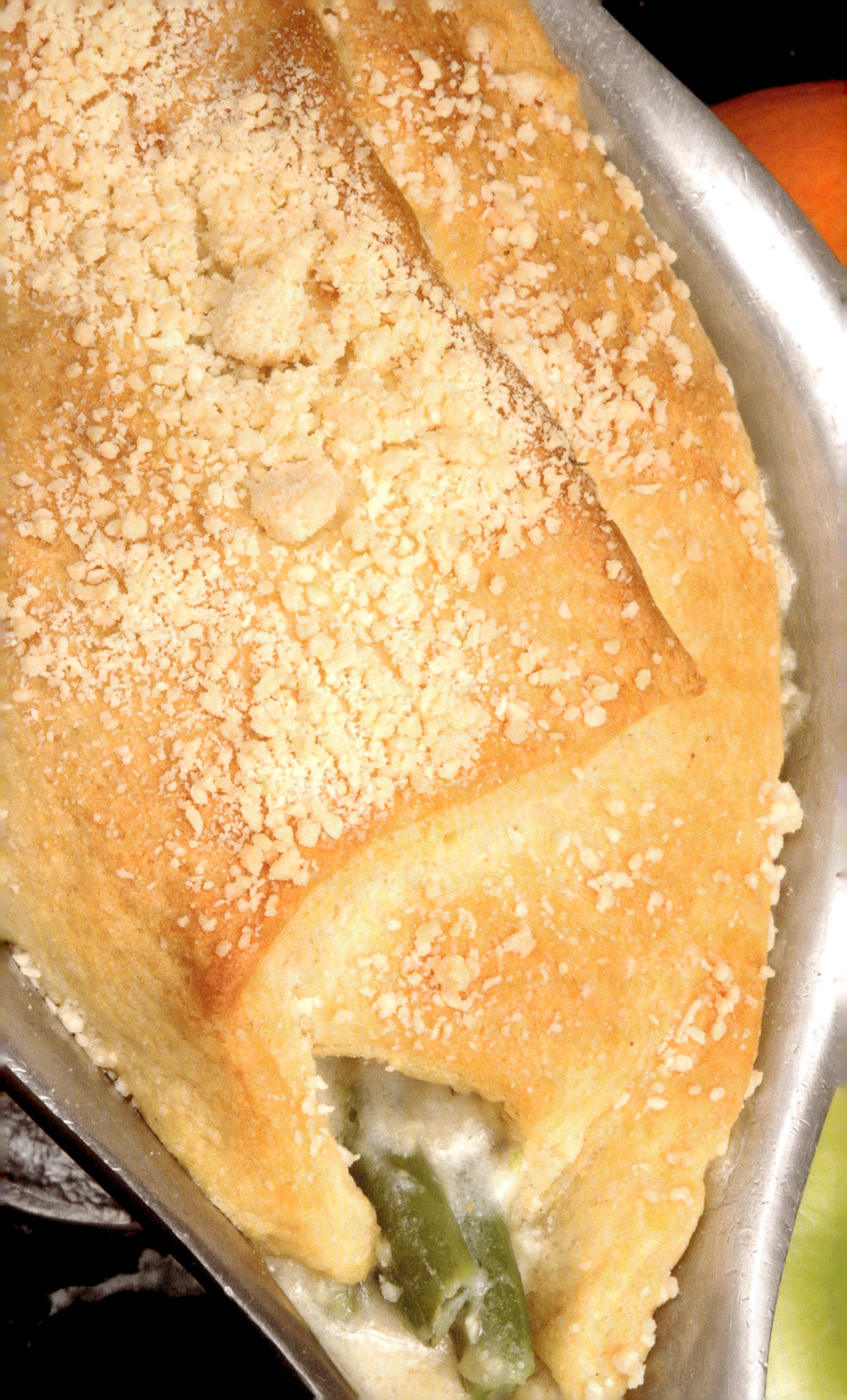

SAVORY PORK CHOP PIE

Make your own Italian seasoning by combining equal amounts of dried oregano and basil.

Equipment Needed:

6-quart stock pot
9x13 baking dish

1/2 tablespoon Vegetable oil
1 1/2 pounds Boneless pork chops, cut into 1/2 inch pieces
2 tablespoons Butter
2 tablespoons All-purpose flour
1 can, 14.5 ounces, Reduced-sodium chicken broth
3/4 cup Buttermilk, low fat
1 1/2 cups Carrot, shredded
1 1/2 cups Green beans, frozen

1/2 cup Red bell pepper, chopped
1/2 cup Green onion, sliced
1/2 teaspoon Dried Italian seasoning
1/4 teaspoon Salt
1/8 teaspoon Pepper
1/8 teaspoon Ground nutmeg
1 can, 8 ounces, Refrigerated reduced-fat crescent rolls
1/4 cup Parmesan cheese, grated

Ideas for Making a Balanced Meal:

Serve with a leafy green salad with mushrooms and orange sherbet

or

Serve with a salad of sliced cucumbers and tomatoes and warm applesauce

1. Preheat oven to 375°.

2. Heat oil in 6-quart stock pot. Sauté pork over medium heat while stirring, about 4 minutes, until no longer pink. Remove meat from pot.

3. Add butter to pot, and melt over medium-high heat. Add flour and stir until it makes a paste. Add broth. Continue to stir until sauce thickens. Add buttermilk.

4. Add pork, carrots, green beans, red pepper, green onion, Italian seasoning, salt, pepper, and nutmeg. Mix well.

5. Pour mixture into a 9 x 13 ungreased baking dish.

6. Separate rolls into triangles, and place on top of mixture. Sprinkle with Parmesan cheese.

7. Bake for 20-25 minutes, or until crust is golden brown.

Serves: 8

Recipe Nutrition per serving:

332 calories; 23 gm protein; 20 gm carbohydrates; 17 gm total fat;
6 gm saturated fat; 58 mg cholesterol; 2 gm fiber; 556 mg sodium.

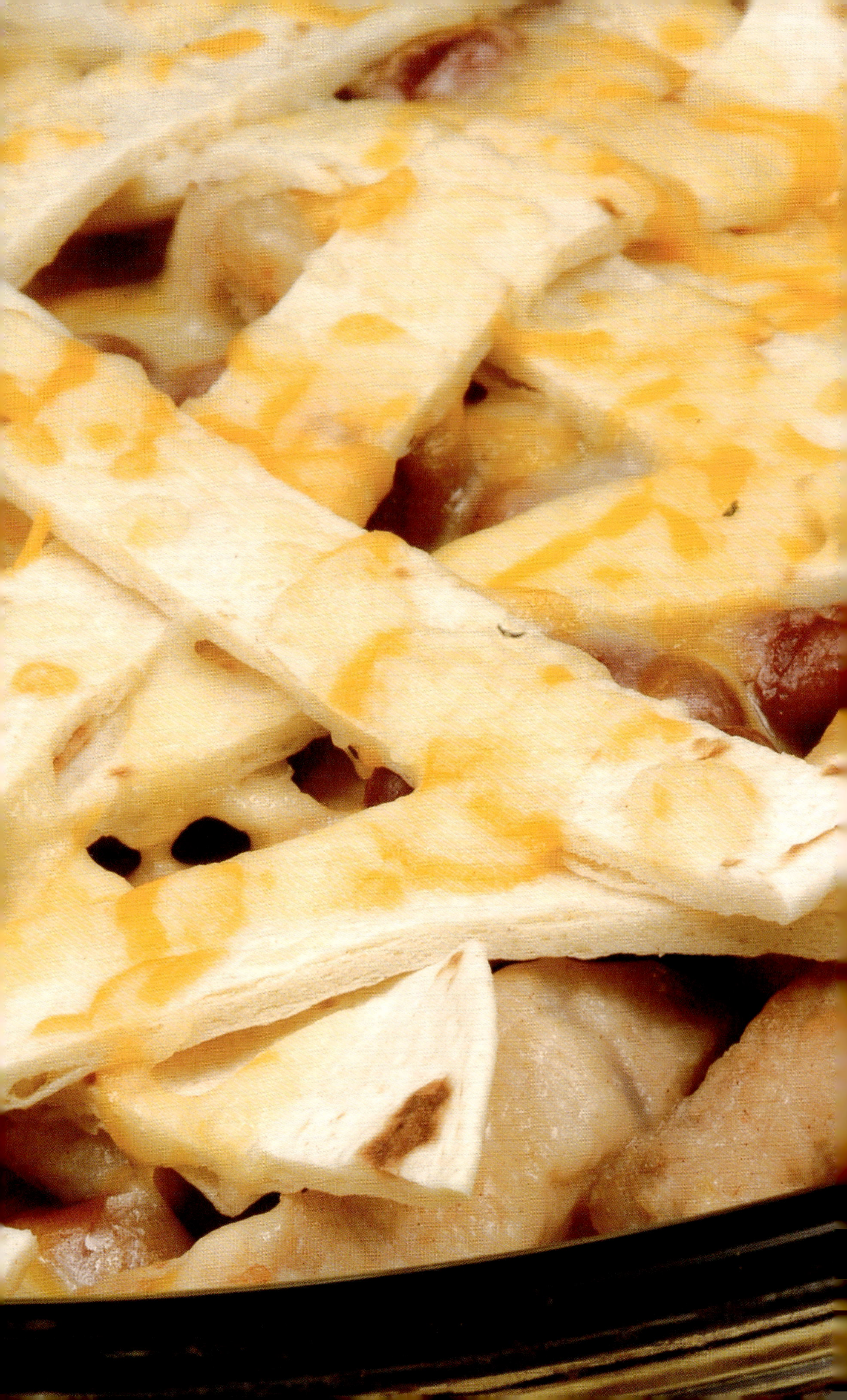

Southwest Enchilada Casserole

For a spicier version, add some chopped jalapeño peppers to the mix or top with salsa.

Equipment Needed:

12-inch skillet
2-quart baking dish

- 1 tablespoon Vegetable oil
- 2 Boneless pork chops, cut into 1/2 inch strips
- 1 can, 10.75 ounces, Southwest style pepper jack soup, condensed
- 1/2 cup Water
- 1/2 teaspoon Garlic powder
- 1/2 teaspoon Dried parsley
- 1 can, 15-16 ounces, Light red kidney beans, rinsed and drained
- 4, 8-inch, Flour tortillas, cut into 1-inch strips
- 3/4 cup Mexican blend cheese, shredded

Ideas for Making a Balanced Meal:

Serve with a sliced avocado and tomato salad and fresh orange

or

Serve with a tossed salad and chilled melon wedge

1. Preheat oven to 350°.

2. Heat oil in a 12-inch skillet. Sauté pork strips in oil over medium heat for about 4 minutes until no longer pink.

3. Add soup, water, garlic powder, parsley and beans to the skillet and stir to combine. Stir in the strips from 3 tortillas.

4. Pour mixture into a 2-quart baking dish. Top with the remaining tortilla strips.

5. Sprinkle cheese over top. Bake for 25 minutes.

Serves: 4

Recipe Nutrition per serving:

449 calories; 29 gm protein; 38 gm carbohydrates; 27 gm total fat; 12 gm saturated fat; 71 mg cholesterol; **4 gm fiber**; 1323 mg sodium.

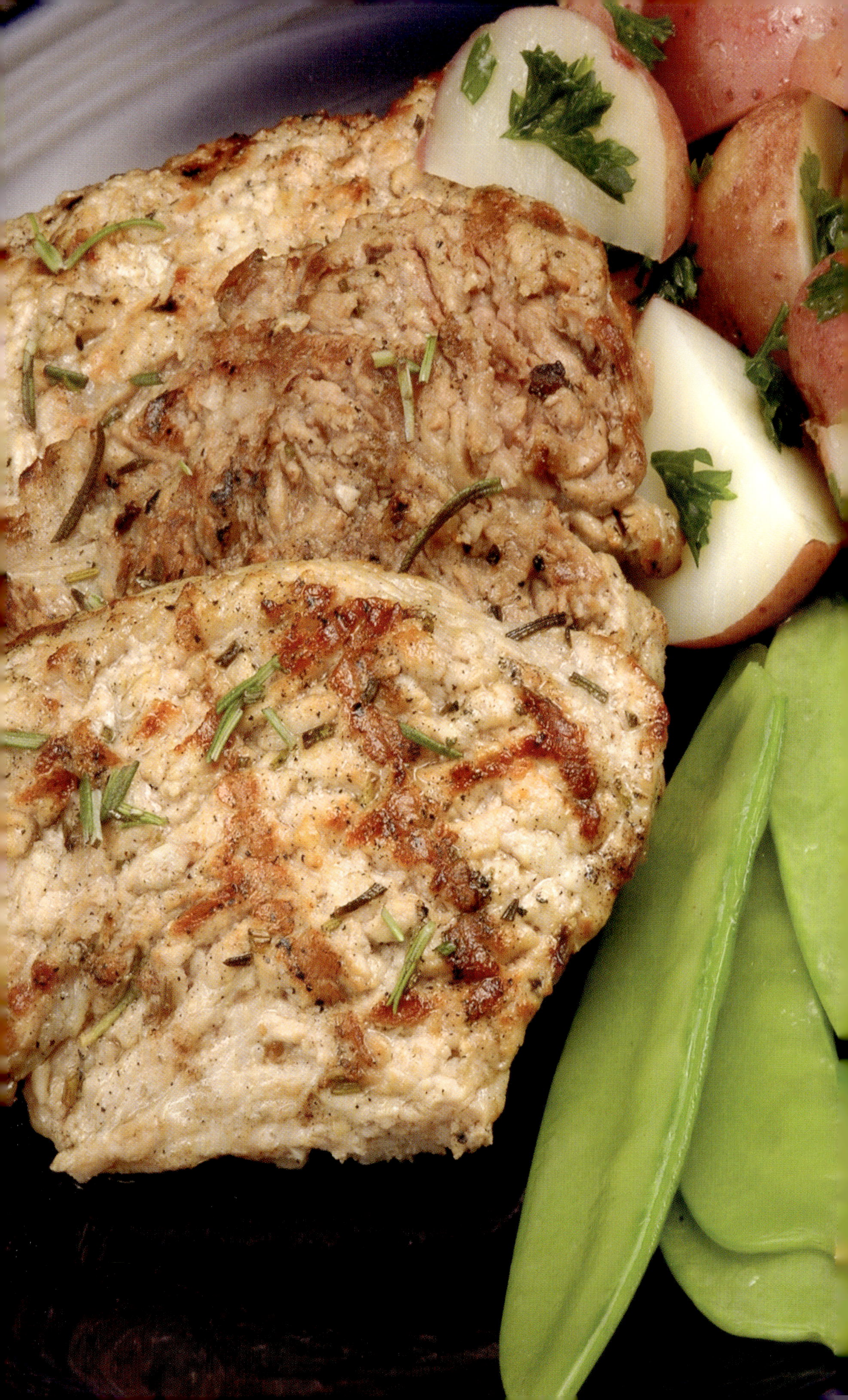

MARINATED PORK CUTLETS

Fresh rosemary gives this marinade a flavor to savor.

Equipment Needed:

12-inch skillet

1/4 cup Lemon juice
1/4 cup Olive Oil
2 cloves Garlic, minced
1 1/2 tablespoons Rosemary, minced
1/4 teaspoon Salt
1/4 teaspoon Pepper
1 pound Boneless pork cutlets
1 tablespoon Olive oil

Ideas for Making a Balanced Meal:

Serve with boiled parsley potatoes, steamed snow peas and fresh watermelon

or

Serve with colorful sautéed sweet peppers and a whole grain roll

1. Mix together the lemon juice, olive oil (1/4 cup), garlic, rosemary, salt and pepper in a small bowl.

2. Place pork cutlets in a pan or dish in one layer.

3. Pour the marinade over the pork and turn meat to coat with marinade.

4. Cover pork and marinate in the refrigerator for 1-2 hours.

5. Heat remaining oil (1 tablespoon) in a 12-inch skillet over medium-high heat. Add pork and cook for 3-4 minutes per side, until meat reaches 160°.

Serves: 4

🍏 *Recipe Nutrition per serving:*

292 calories; 22 gm protein; 1 gm carbohydrate; 22 gm total fat; 6 gm saturated fat; 68 mg cholesterol; 0 gm fiber; **127 mg sodium**.

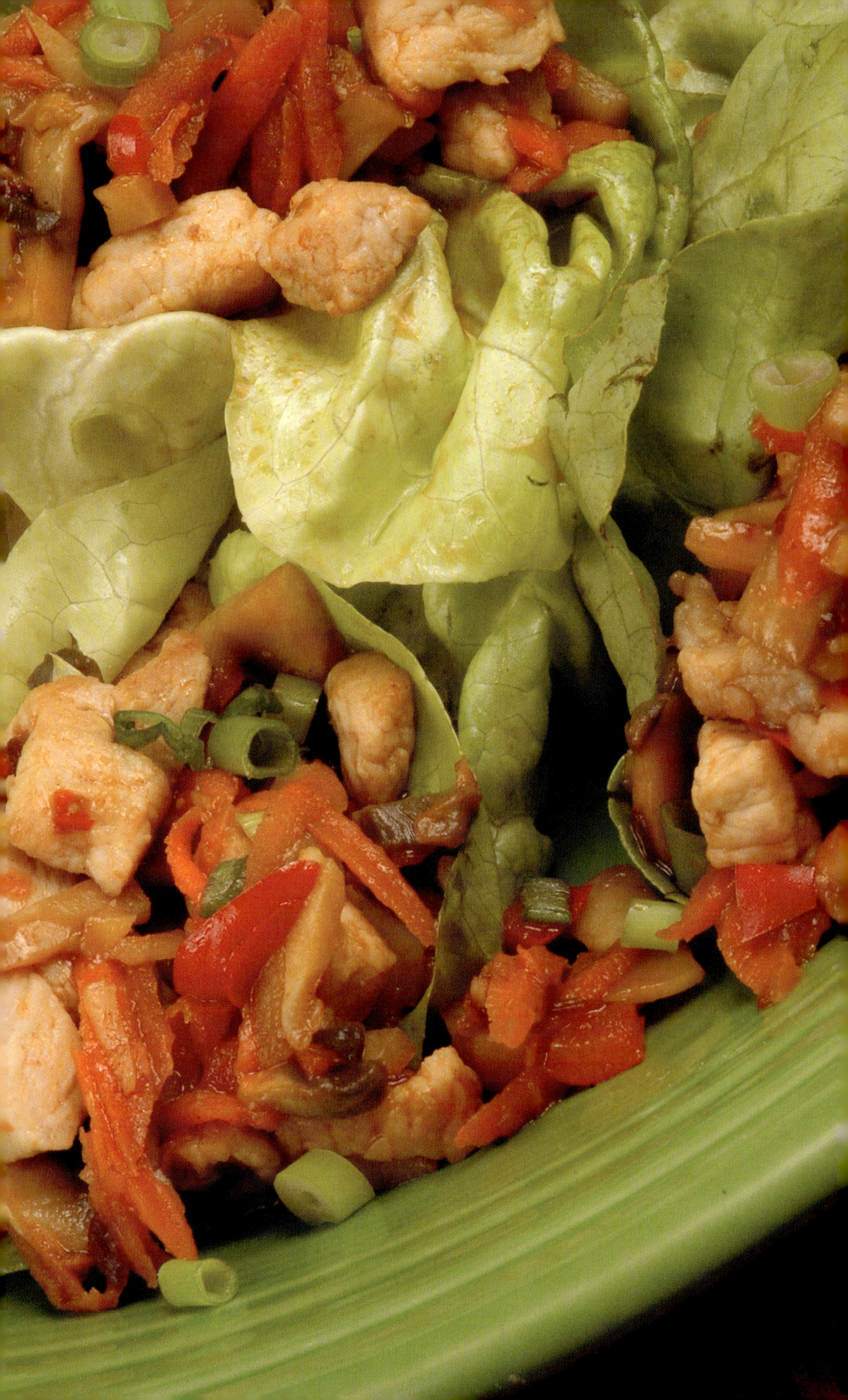

SPICY PORK LETTUCE WRAPS

Serve this recipe with lime wedges and chopped cilantro.

Equipment Needed:

12-inch skillet

Sauce:
2 tablespoons Oyster sauce
2 tablespoons Water
1 tablespoon Hoisin sauce
1 tablespoon Dry sherry or sake
1 teaspoon Brown sugar
1 teaspoon Reduced-sodium soy sauce
1 teaspoon Sesame oil

Stir-fry:
3 teaspoons Canola oil
4 Boneless, center cut loin chops, cut into 1/2-inch cubes
2 cloves Garlic, minced
1 tablespoon Ginger, minced
1 1/2 teaspoons Red chile paste with garlic
1 can, 8 ounces, Water chestnuts, coarsely chopped
1 can, 8 ounces, Bamboo shoots, coarsely chopped
1/2 cup Mushrooms, thinly sliced
1/4 cup Carrot, shredded
1/4 cup Red pepper, diced
1/4 cup Green onion, sliced
1 head Boston lettuce

Garnish:
Chopped green onions

Ideas for Making a Balanced Meal:

Serve with pasta salad, pickle slices and fresh blueberries

or

Serve with white or brown rice, steamed zucchini and fresh mango slices

1. Prepare sauce by combining all ingredients in a small bowl.

2. Heat 2 teaspoons oil over medium-high heat in a 12-inch skillet. Add pork and cook, stirring constantly, until no longer pink, about 4 minutes. Transfer to a plate, wipe out pan.

3. Add remaining 1 teaspoon oil, garlic, ginger and chile paste to skillet; cook, stirring constantly, for 30 seconds.

4. Add water chestnuts, bamboo shoots, mushrooms, carrot, red pepper, and green onion. Stir often, until the mushrooms have softened.

5. Return pork to the pan and add the sauce. Stir constantly until the sauce has completely coated the pork and vegetables.

6. Spoon 1/2 cup filling into a lettuce leaf. Sprinkle with chopped green onions.

Serves: 6

Recipe Nutrition per serving:

197 calories; 17 gm protein; 10 gm carbohydrates; **10 gm total fat**; **2 gm saturated fat**; 48 mg cholesterol; 2 gm fiber; **155 mg sodium**.

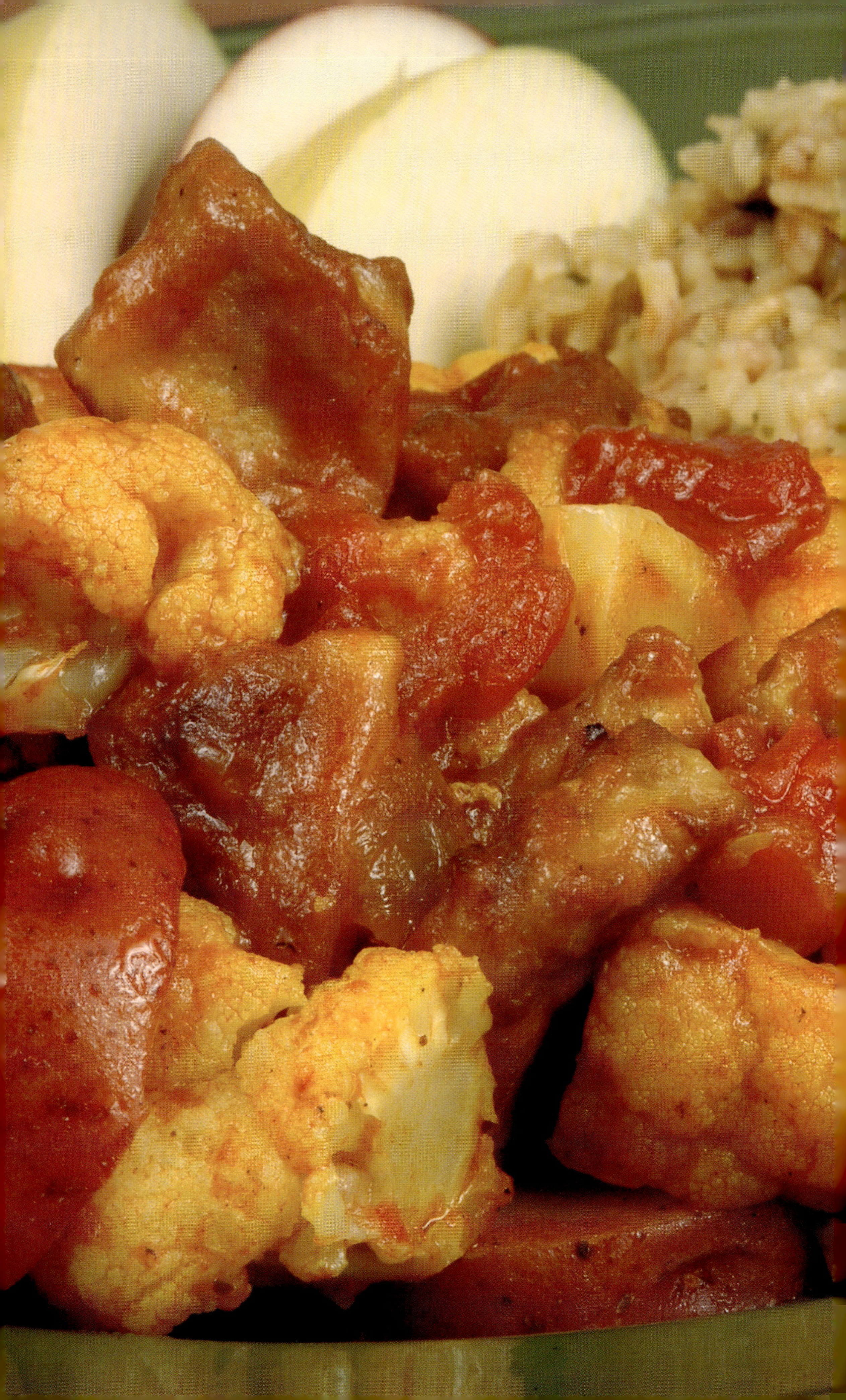

CURRIED PORK STEW
Leftovers taste even better the next day for lunch!

Equipment Needed:
12-inch skillet
Slow-cooker or crock pot

1 pound Boneless loin chops, cut into 1-inch pieces
3 tablespoons All purpose flour
3 tablespoons Curry powder
1/2 teaspoon Salt
1/2 teaspoon Pepper
1 tablespoon Olive oil
1 medium Onion, chopped
1 pound Small red potatoes
1 can, 14.5 ounces, Whole tomatoes, with juice
1/2 cup Apple juice
1 cup Cauliflower, cut into small pieces

Ideas for Making a Balanced Meal:

Serve with couscous and fresh apple slices

or

Serve with a tossed green salad and pineapple slices

1. Combine flour, curry powder, salt and pepper in a shallow dish. Coat pork pieces with flour mixture.

2. Heat oil in a 12-inch skillet. Brown pork over medium-high heat.

3. Layer potatoes, onions, pork and tomatoes in slow-cooker.

4. Pour apple juice into slow-cooker.

5. Cover and cook on low for 7 hours.

6. Add cauliflower and cook one more hour or until tender.

Serves: 6

🍏 *Recipe Nutrition per serving:*

248 calories; 18 gm protein; 24 gm carbohydrates; **9 gm total fat**; **2 gm saturated fat**; 48 mg cholesterol; **4 gm fiber**; 333 mg sodium.

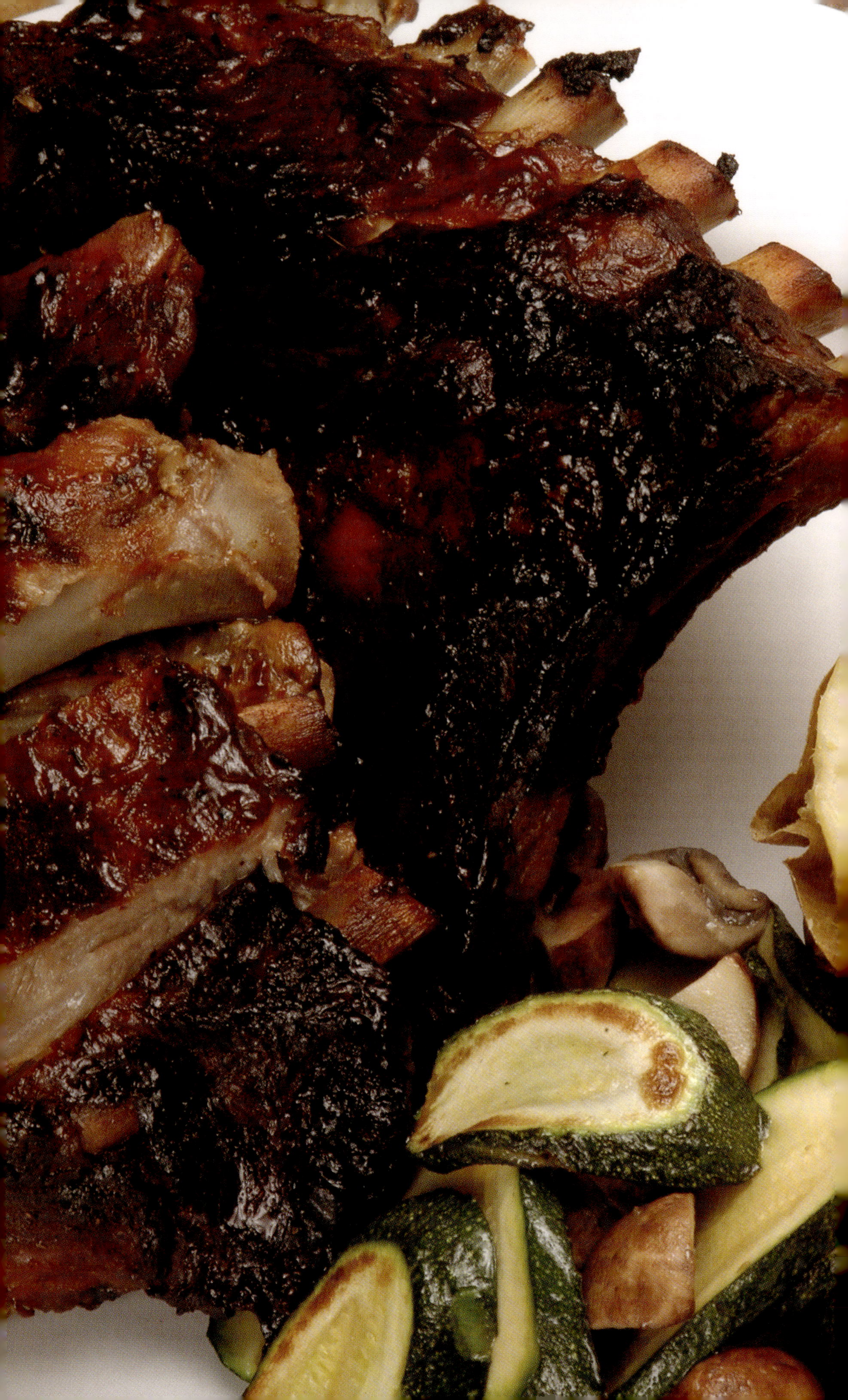

EASY OVEN BAKED RIBS

These ribs also can be cooked on the grill.

Equipment Needed:

Roasting pan

3 pounds Baby back ribs
2 cups Bottled barbecue sauce

Ideas for Making a Balanced Meal:

Serve with a baked potato, steamed beets and spinach salad

or

Serve with lima beans and a salad of colorful bell pepper slices

1. Preheat oven to 325°.

2. Cover ribs with sauce and turn to coat.

3. Place ribs meat side up in roasting pan.

4. Roast in the middle of the oven, basting with sauce every 20 minutes until tender, about 1 3/4 hours. Discard any unused sauce.

5. Cut into individual ribs and serve.

Serves: 6

Recipe Nutrition per serving:

454 calories; 27 gm protein; 12 gm carbohydrates; 32 gm total fat; 12 gm saturated fat; 122 mg cholesterol; 1 gm fiber; 865 mg sodium.

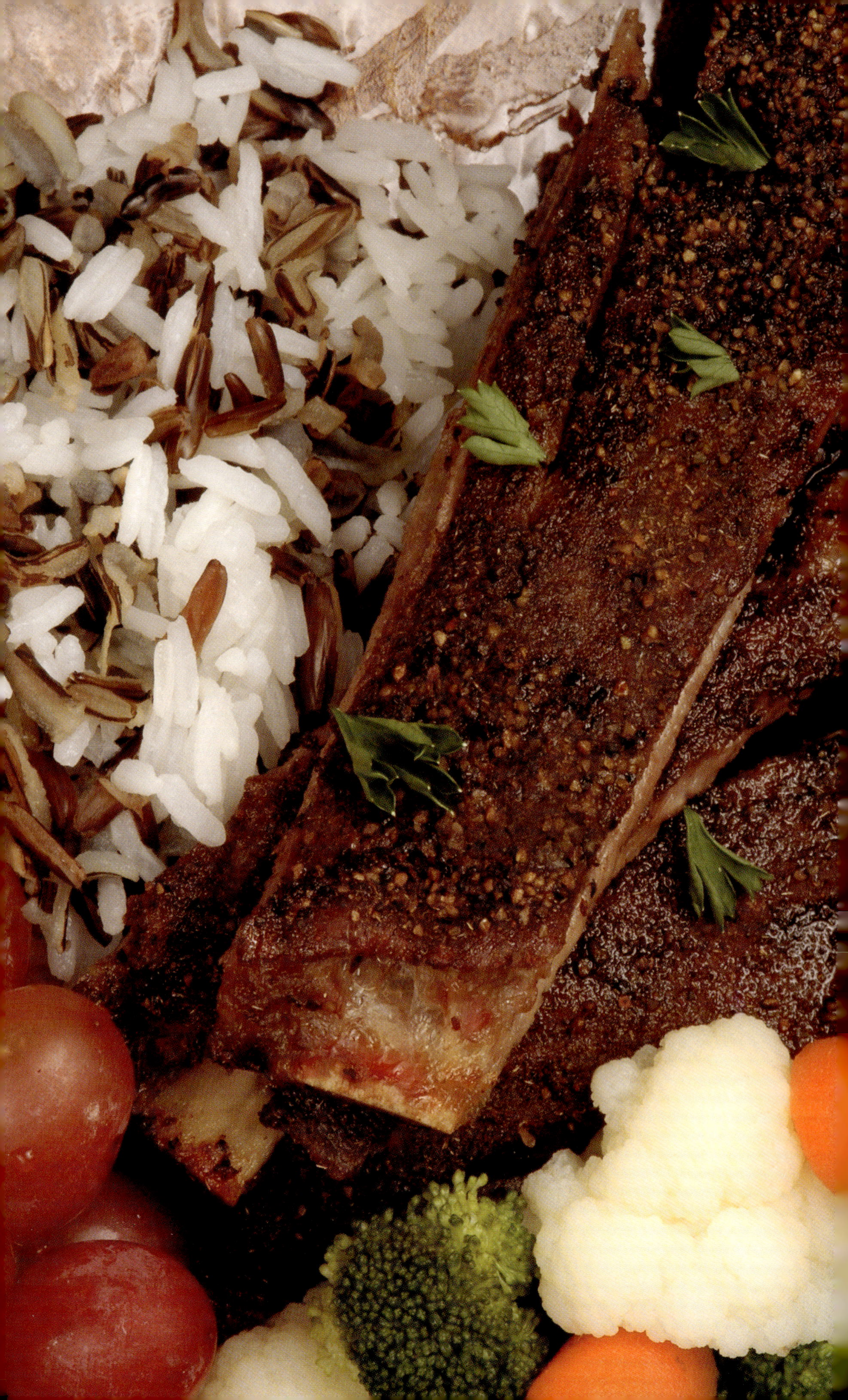

JERK PORK RIBS

This Caribbean island-flavored recipe will please any group!

Equipment Needed:

Roasting pan

- 2 pounds Spare ribs
- 1 tablespoon Onion powder
- 1 tablespoon Garlic powder
- 4 teaspoons Ground thyme
- 2 teaspoons Salt
- 2 teaspoons Ground allspice
- 1/2 teaspoon Ground nutmeg
- 1/2 teaspoon Ground cinnamon
- 1 tablespoon Sugar
- 2 teaspoons Pepper
- 1 teaspoon Cayenne pepper

Ideas for Making a Balanced Meal:

Serve with wild rice, a blend of steamed cauliflower and broccoli and fresh grapes

or

Serve with steamed corn, a sliced cucumber and onion salad and a plum

1. Combine all dry ingredients in a small bowl. Stir until blended.

2. Rub dry mixture onto all surfaces of ribs.

3. Roast ribs in a roasting pan at 350° for 1 1/2 to 2 hours. Cut ribs into 1 or 2 rib portions.

Serves: 6

Recipe Nutrition per serving:

305 calories; 21 gm protein; 6 gm carbohydrates; 22 gm total fat; 8 gm saturated fat; 85 mg cholesterol; 1 gm fiber; 843 mg sodium.

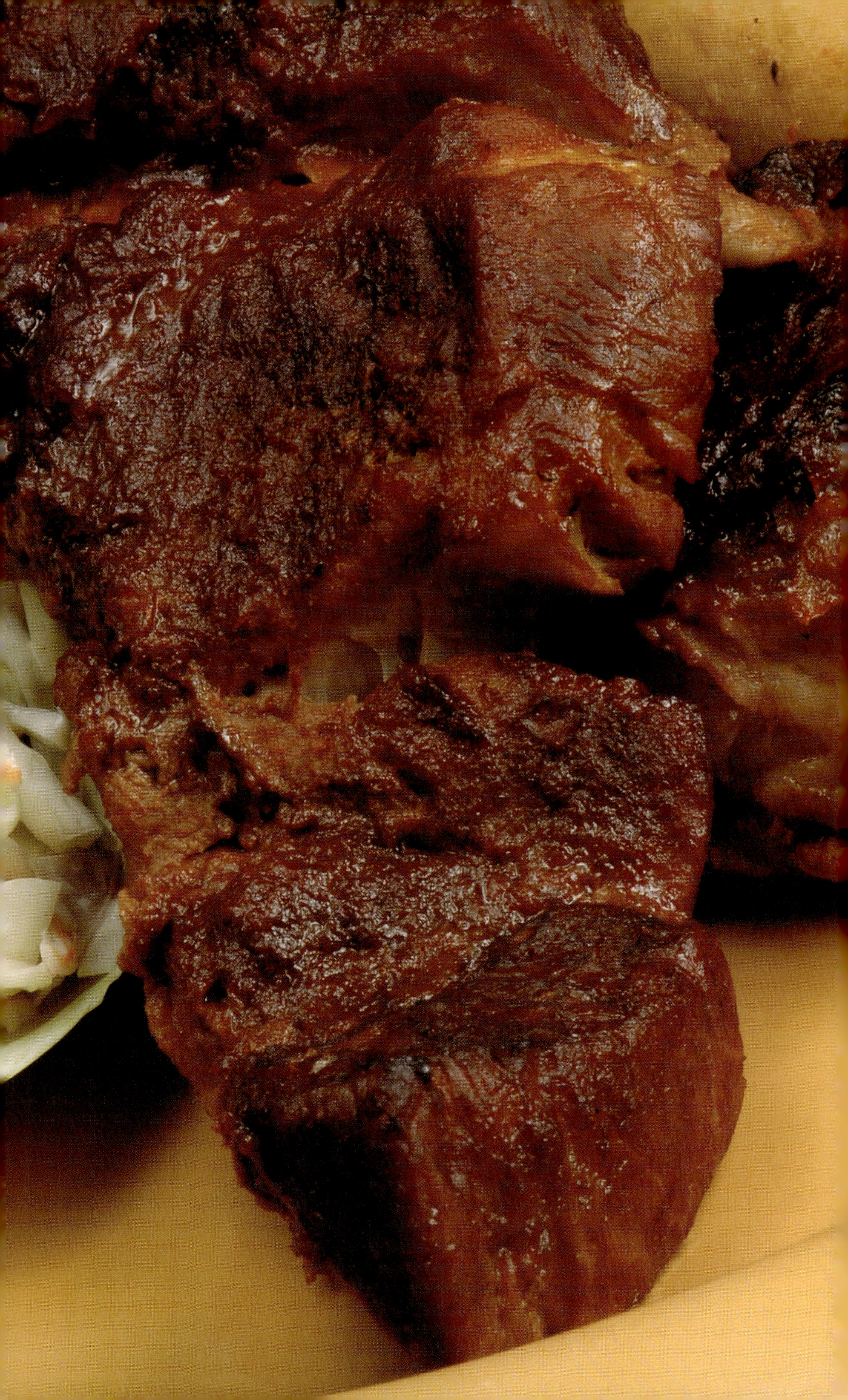

Oven Barbecued Country Style Ribs

This is an easy way to prepare delicious ribs.

Equipment Needed:

Roasting pan

4 pounds Country style ribs

Sauce:
1/2 cup Ketchup
1 1/2 teaspoons Salt
1/2 teaspoon Hot pepper sauce
2 tablespoons Brown sugar
1/8 teaspoon Chili powder
1 cup Water
1 large Onion, chopped

Ideas for Making a Balanced Meal:

Serve with baked French fries and a colorful tossed salad

or

Serve with fresh bread slices, cole slaw, and chilled watermelon

1. Preheat oven to 350°. Place ribs in a roasting pan.

2. Mix sauce ingredients in a small bowl and pour over meat. Cover pan with aluminum foil.

3. Bake for approximately 3 hours or until ribs are tender.

Serves: 12

🍏 Recipe Nutrition per serving:

272 calories; 19 gm protein; 3 gm carbohydrates; 20 gm total fat; 7 gm saturated fat; 73 mg cholesterol; 0 gm fiber; **245 mg sodium**.

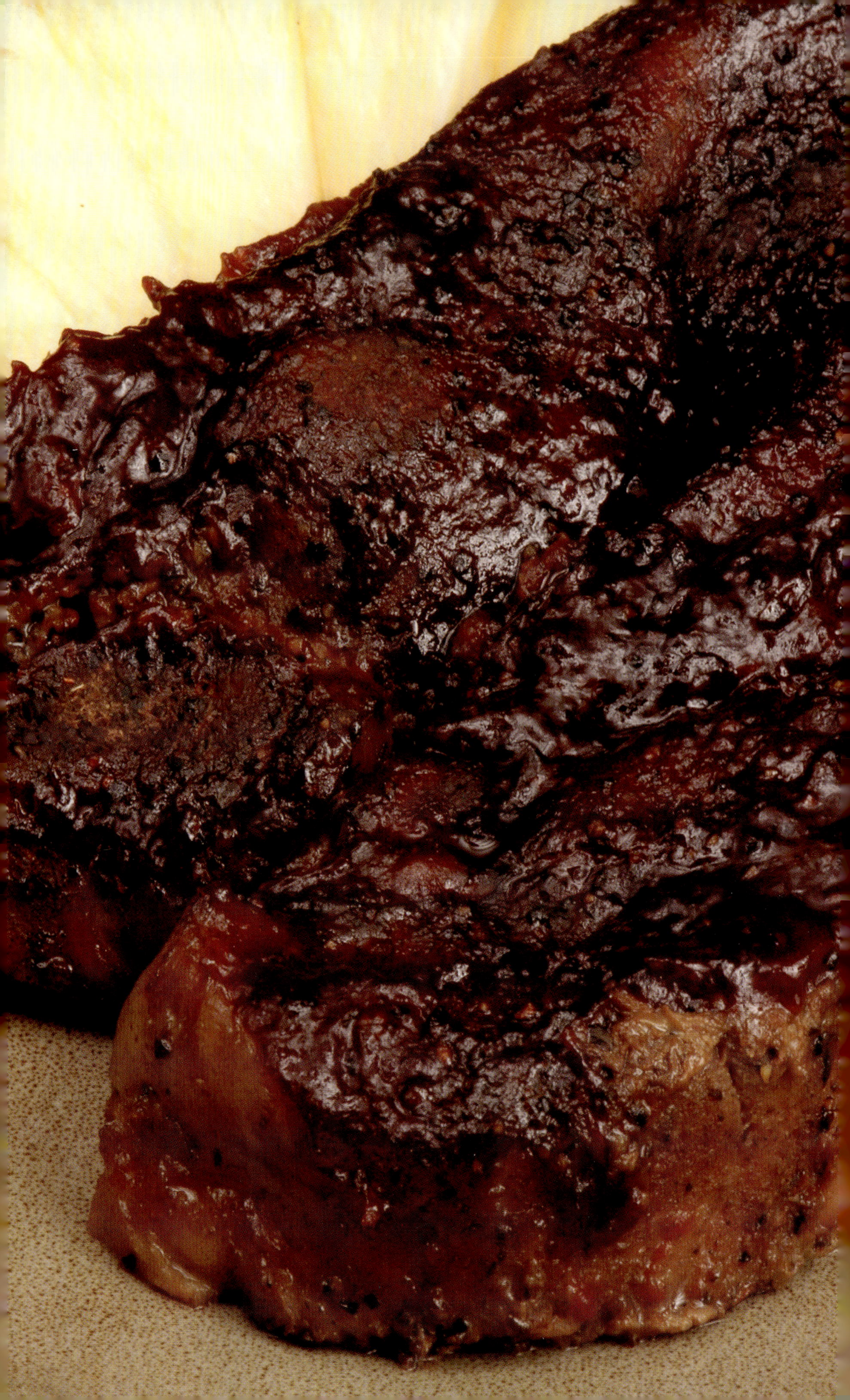

STICKY PORK RIBS

These ribs can also be cooked on the grill.

Equipment Needed:

Roasting pan

- 3/4 cup Ketchup
- 1/4 cup Molasses
- 2 tablespoons Lemon juice
- 2 tablespoons Reduced-sodium soy sauce
- 1/4 teaspoon Hot pepper sauce
- 2 tablespoons Brown sugar
- 2 teaspoons Chinese five-spice powder
- 1 teaspoon Ground cloves
- 1/2 teaspoon Ground coriander
- 1 teaspoon Salt
- 1 teaspoon Paprika
- 1/2 teaspoon Pepper
- 3 pounds Country style ribs

Ideas for Making a Balanced Meal:

Serve with steamed sugar snap peas, fresh bread and cantaloupe

or

Serve with cole slaw, potato salad and fresh strawberries

1. Preheat oven to 350°.

2. Combine ketchup, molasses, lemon juice, soy sauce, and hot pepper sauce in a bowl and set aside.

3. Combine brown sugar, five-spice powder, cloves, coriander, salt, paprika, and pepper in a bowl. Rub dry mixture onto ribs, coating ribs completely.

4. Place ribs in a foil-lined roasting pan and cover with foil. Roast for 2 hours, and then brush molasses sauce on ribs. Cook, uncovered, for 30 minutes longer.

Serves: 9

Recipe Nutrition per serving:

324 calories; 19 gm protein; 16 gm carbohydrates; 20 gm total fat; 7 gm saturated fat; 73 mg cholesterol; 0 gm fiber; 664 mg sodium.

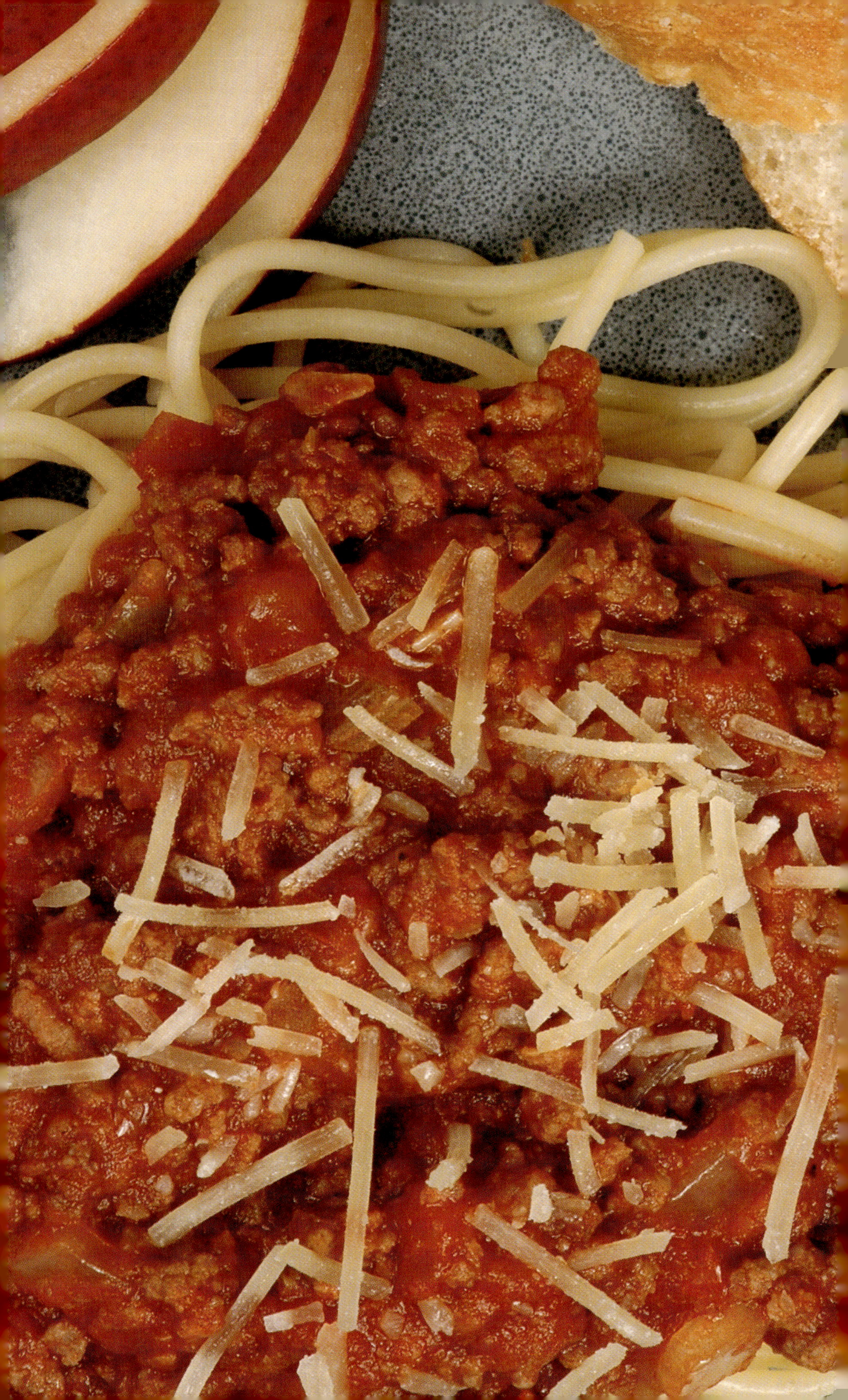

Homemade Pasta Sauce

Make a double batch and freeze one for a quick dinner later on.

Equipment Needed:

Two 6-quart pots

1 tablespoon Olive oil
1 clove Garlic, minced
1 medium Onion, chopped
1 pound Lean ground pork
2 cans, 6 ounces, Tomato paste
3 cups Hot water
1 can, 28 ounces, Diced tomatoes
1 pound Dried pasta

Ideas for Making a Balanced Meal:

Serve over hot pasta with fresh bread and steamed sugar snap peas

or

Serve over a bun with pasta salad, a sliced tomato salad and a fresh pear

1. Heat oil in a 6-quart pot over medium-high heat. Add garlic and onion, and sauté for 2-3 minutes.

2. Add pork to pot and sauté 6-8 minutes, until pork is no longer pink. Drain fat.

3. Add tomato paste and hot water to pot. Stir until tomato paste is completely dissolved. Add diced tomatoes. Bring to a boil, then reduce heat to medium.

4. Simmer 10 minutes, stirring frequently.

5. Cook pasta according to package directions. Serve with sauce.

Serves: 8

Recipe Nutrition per serving:

387 calories; 20 gm protein; 53 gm carbohydrates; 11 gm total fat;
4 gm saturated fat; 38 mg cholesterol; **5 gm fiber**; 638 mg sodium.

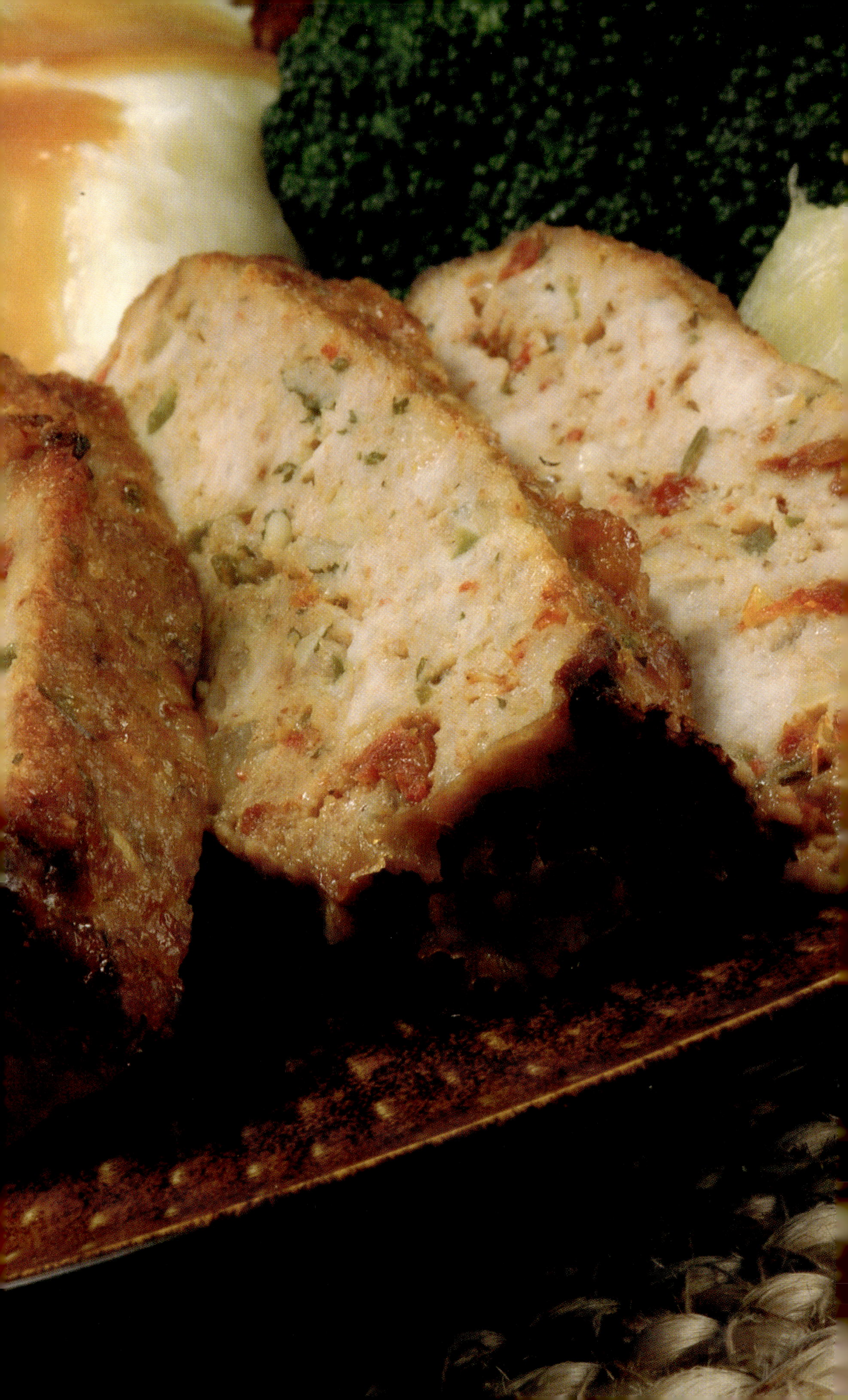

Southwestern Meat Loaf

Cook a double batch and freeze one for a quick meal.

Equipment Needed:

Large mixing bowl
9x5x3 loaf pan

1 1/2 pounds Lean ground pork
1 large Onion, finely chopped
3 cloves Garlic, minced
2 tablespoons Jalapeño pepper, minced
1/4 cup Sun-dried tomatoes, minced
1 tablespoon Chile powder
1 teaspoon Ground cumin
1 1/2 teaspoons Salt
1 teaspoon Dried Thyme
1/2 teaspoon Cayenne pepper
1/2 cup Parsley, finely chopped
1/2 cup Plain bread crumbs
1/2 cup Skim milk

1. Preheat oven to 350º.

2. Place ground pork in a large mixing bowl. Add remaining ingredients and combine.

3. Place mixture in a 9x5x3 loaf pan and bake for approximately 1 1/2 hours, until meat thermometer reads 160º.

Serves: 8

Recipe Nutrition per serving:

233 calories; 18 gm protein; 9 gm carbohydrates; 14 gm total fat; 5 gm saturated fat; 57 mg cholesterol; 1 gm fiber; 552 mg sodium.

Ideas for Making a Balanced Meal:

Serve with mashed potatoes, steamed broccoli and fresh pineapple chunks

or

Serve with couscous, steamed greens and fresh strawberries

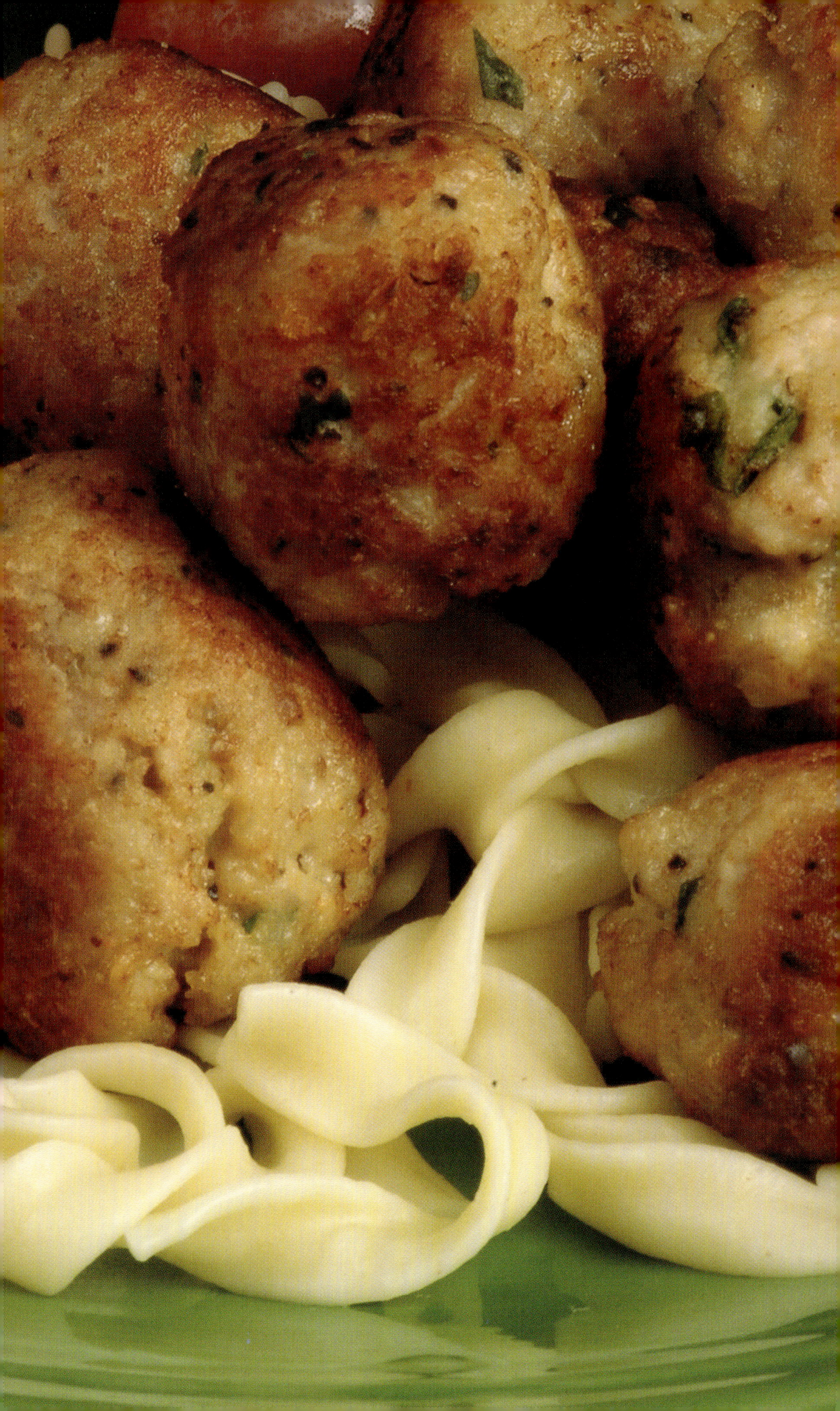

Easy Pork Meatballs

Serve with your favorite tomato sauce for a meal the whole family will enjoy.

Equipment Needed:

12-inch skillet

1 pound Lean ground pork
1/2 cup Bread crumbs
1/4 cup Parmesan cheese, grated
2 cloves Garlic, minced
1/2 cup Parsley leaves, chopped

1/2 teaspoon Salt
1/2 teaspoon Pepper
1 Egg, lightly beaten
1/4 cup Vegetable oil

Ideas for Making a Balanced Meal:

Serve with mashed potatoes, green beans and sliced fresh oranges

or

Serve on a hard roll with cole slaw and chilled melon

1. In a medium bowl, combine all ingredients and mix. Be careful not to over mix.

2. Shape mixture into 1-inch balls.

3. In a 12-inch skillet, heat oil over high heat. Add meatballs to fill the skillet (you may need to cook them in more than 1 batch). Cook until brown on bottom; turn meatballs. Repeat process until meatballs are brown on all sides and cooked through, about 10 minutes.

4. Remove meatballs from skillet as they are done. Place on paper towel-lined dish to absorb extra fat.

Serves: 6

Recipe Nutrition per serving:

307 calories; 18 gm protein; 7 gm carbohydrates; 23 gm total fat; 6 gm saturated fat; 89 mg cholesterol; 1 gm fiber; 365 mg sodium.

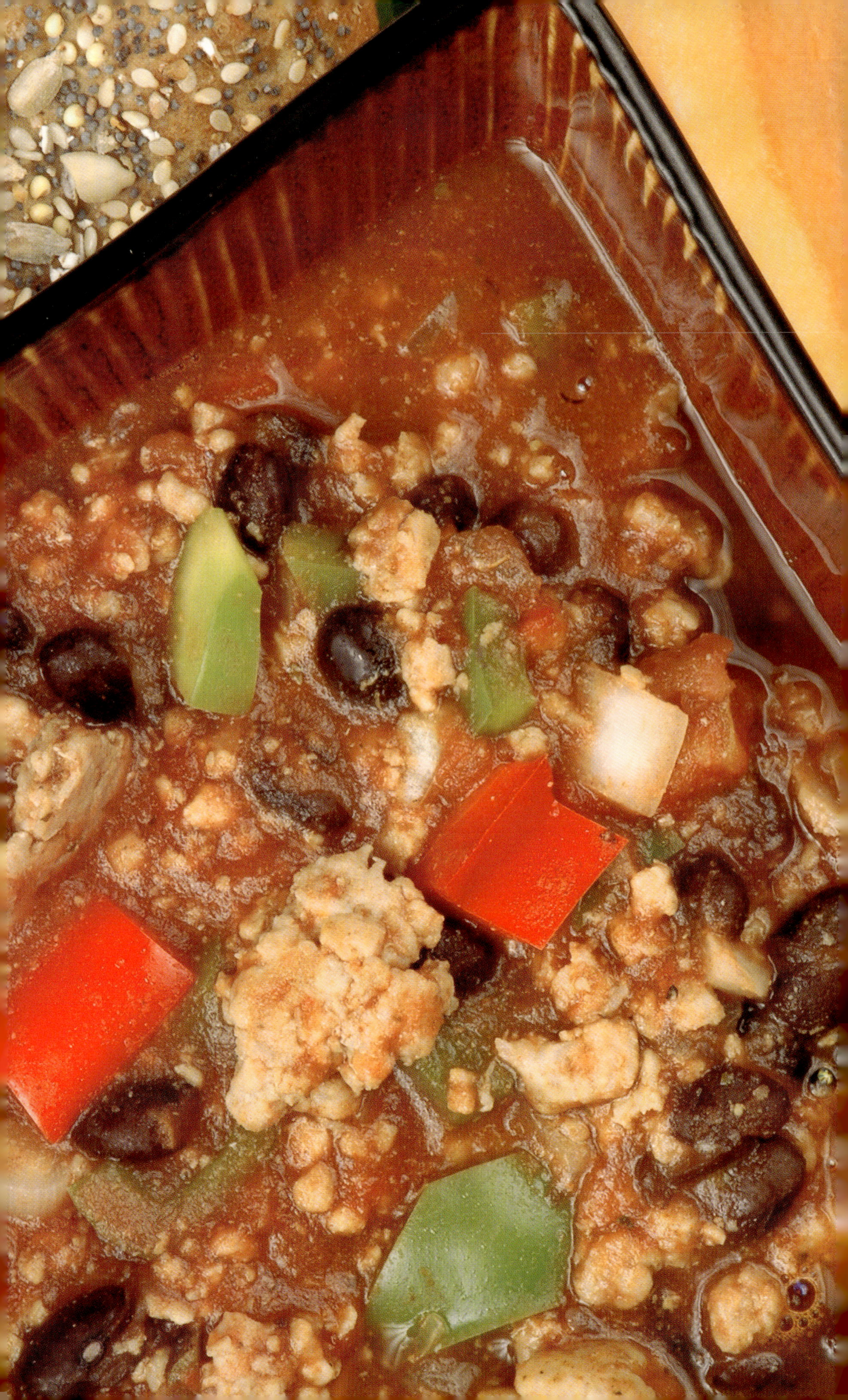

LEAN MEAN CHILI & BEANS
Pair this recipe with cornbread for a complete meal.

Equipment Needed:

3-quart saucepan

1 tablespoon Vegetable oil
1 pound Lean ground pork
3 tablespoons Chili powder
1 tablespoon Cumin
1 1/2 teaspoons Dried oregano
1 teaspoon Salt
1 Onion, chopped
1 Red bell pepper, chopped
1 Green bell pepper, chopped
2 cloves Garlic, minced
1 can, 28 ounces, Crushed tomatoes
1 Cinnamon stick
1 can, 15 ounces, Black beans, drained

Ideas for Making a Balanced Meal:

Serve with baked French fries, red cabbage coleslaw and an orange

or

Serve with whole grain bread, tossed salad and an apple

1. Heat oil in a 3-quart sauce pan over medium-high heat. Brown pork for 7 minutes, stirring often. Drain fat from pork.

2. Add chili powder, cumin, oregano, salt, onion, peppers and garlic to pot and cook for 5 minutes.

3. Add tomatoes and cinnamon. Bring to a simmer, reduce heat to low, cover and cook for 30 minutes, stirring occasionally.

4. Add black beans and cook, uncovered, for 5 minutes.

Serves: 6

Recipe Nutrition per serving:

321 calories; 22 gm protein; 28 gm carbohydrates; 15 gm total fat; 4 gm saturated fat; 50 mg cholesterol; **9 gm fiber**; 606 mg sodium.

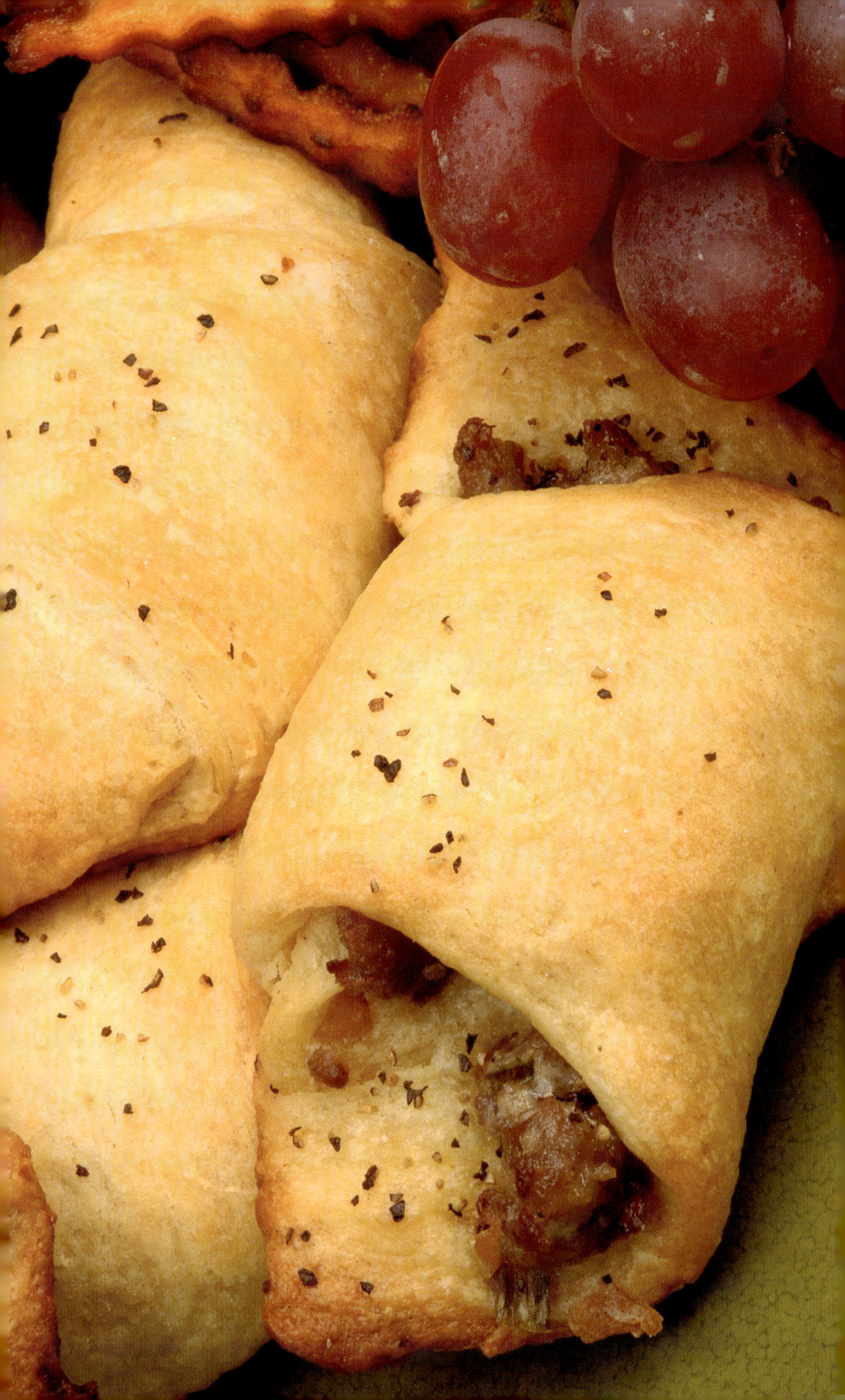

PORK-FILLED CRESCENT ROLLS
Children will have fun helping with this recipe.

Equipment Needed:

12-inch skillet
Large cookie sheet

1 pound Lean ground pork
1/2 cup Mango chutney
1 teaspoon Ground mustard
4 Green onions, sliced

1/2 cup Reduced-fat sour cream
1 can, 8 ounces, Reduced-fat crescent dinner rolls
1/2 teaspoon Pepper

Ideas for Making a Balanced Meal:

Serve with baked sweet potato fries and sliced tomatoes, cucumbers and olives

or

Serve with cole slaw and celery and carrot sticks

1. Heat oven to 350º.

2. Cook ground pork in a 12-inch skillet until no longer pink, about 5 minutes. Drain fat from pork.

3. Add chutney, mustard, onions and sour cream. Mix well.

4. Unroll crescent roll dough onto a cookie sheet, and separate into 6 triangles.

5. Place 1-2 tablespoons of pork mixture on the widest end of each roll.

6. Roll toward the opposite end of the crescent, and leave on cookie sheet. Sprinkle each roll with black pepper.

7. Bake for 20-25 minutes or until golden brown.

Serves: 6

Recipe Nutrition per serving:

362 calories; 18 gm protein; 27 gm carbohydrates; 20 gm total fat; 7 gm saturated fat; 58 mg cholesterol; 1 gm fiber; 364 mg sodium.

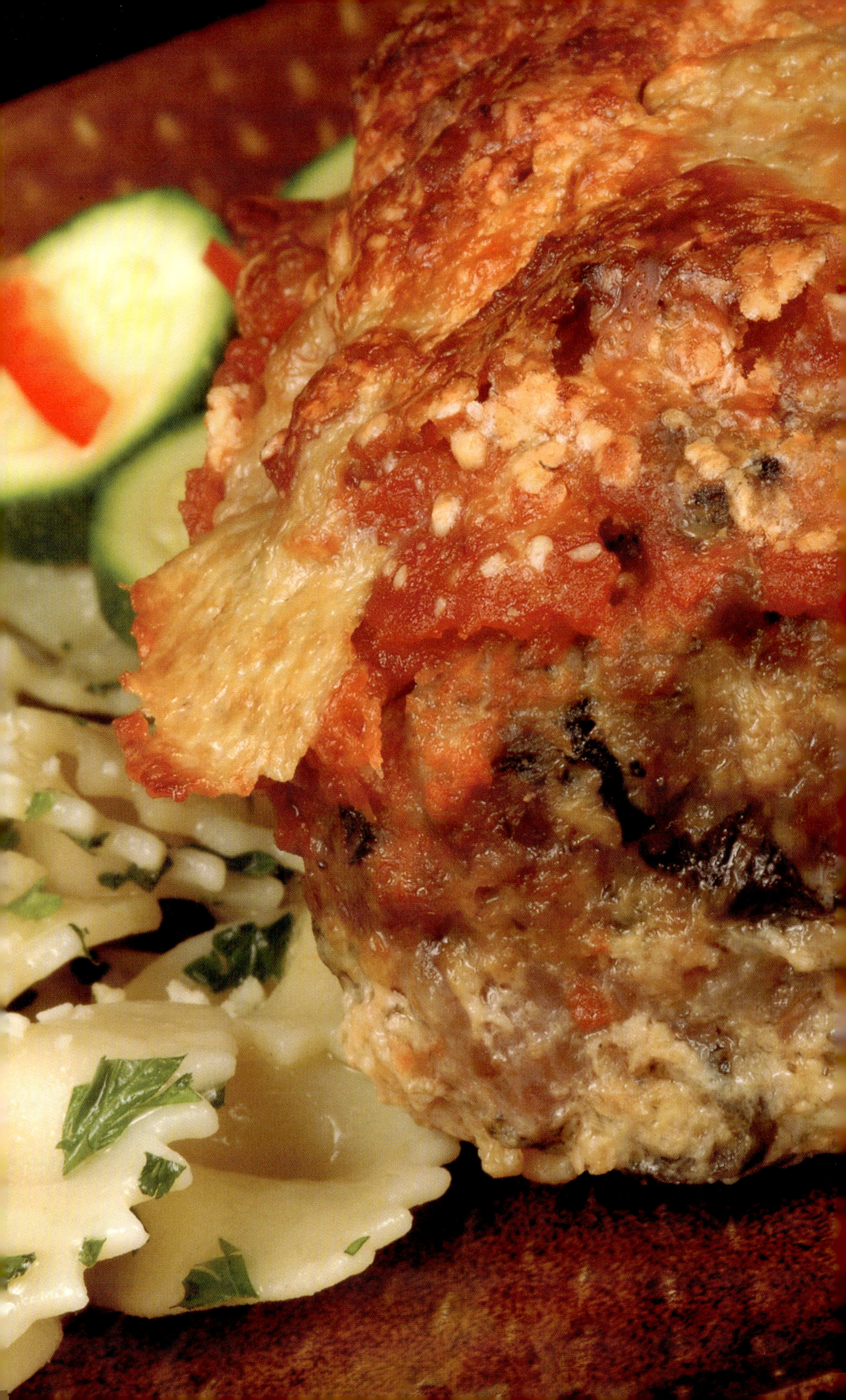

Pork-Spinach Meat Loaf

Leftovers of this recipe make a delicious sandwich on Italian bread.

Equipment Needed:

Large bowl
9x5x3 loaf pan

- 1 1/4 pounds Lean ground pork
- 1 Egg
- 1/2 cup Bread crumbs
- 1 small Onion, diced
- 1/2 teaspoon Salt
- 1/2 teaspoon Pepper
- 1 package, 10 ounces, Frozen spinach, defrosted and liquid squeezed out
- 1 cup Part-skim Mozzarella cheese, shredded
- 1 teaspoon Oregano
- 1 teaspoon Basil
- 2 cloves Garlic, minced
- 1 can, 8 ounces, Tomato sauce
- 1/4 cup Parmesan cheese, grated

Ideas for Making a Balanced Meal:

Serve with lightly buttered noodles and steamed zucchini

or

Serve with white beans, tossed green salad and fresh pear slices

1. Preheat oven to 375°.

2. Combine all ingredients, except tomato sauce and Parmesan cheese, in a large mixing bowl.

3. Shape the mixture into a loaf and place in a 9x5x3 inch loaf pan.

4. Cover the meat loaf with tomato sauce. Sprinkle Parmesan cheese on top.

5. Bake for 50 to 60 minutes, or until meat thermometer reads 160°.

Serves: 8

Recipe Nutrition per serving:

255 calories; 21 gm protein; 9 gm carbohydrates; 15 gm total fat; 6 gm saturated fat; 84 mg cholesterol; 2 gm fiber; 525 mg sodium.

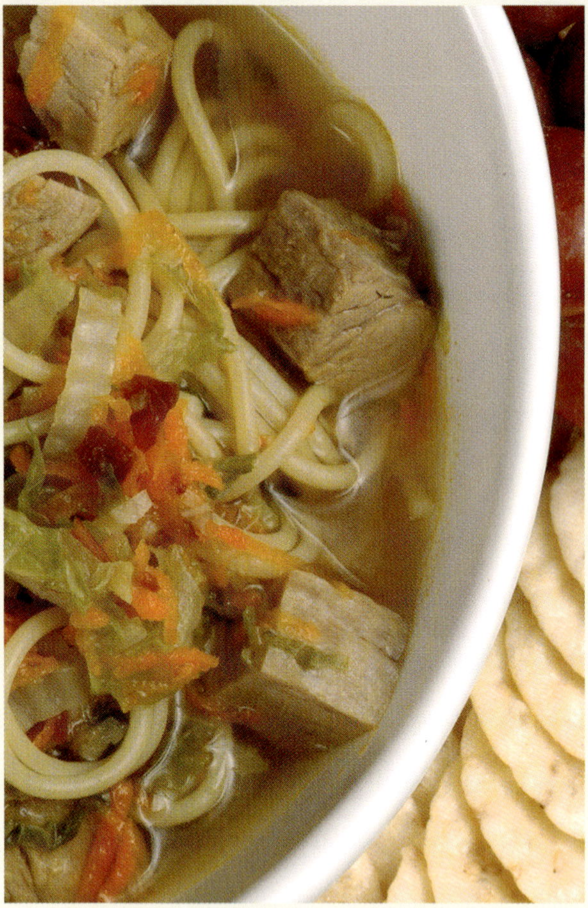
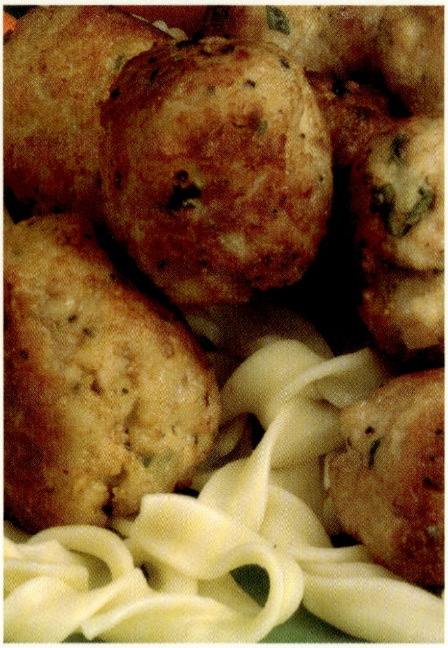
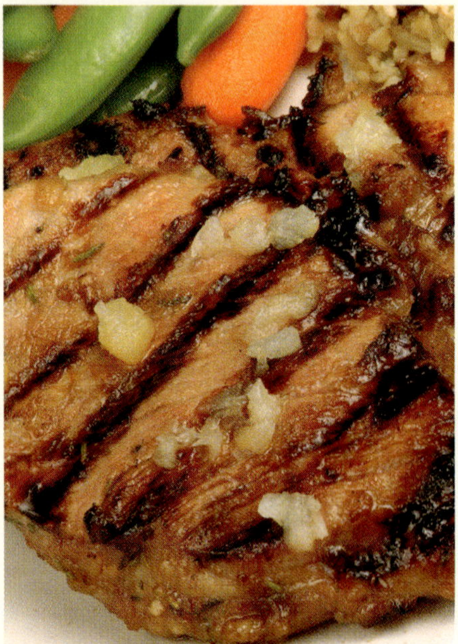
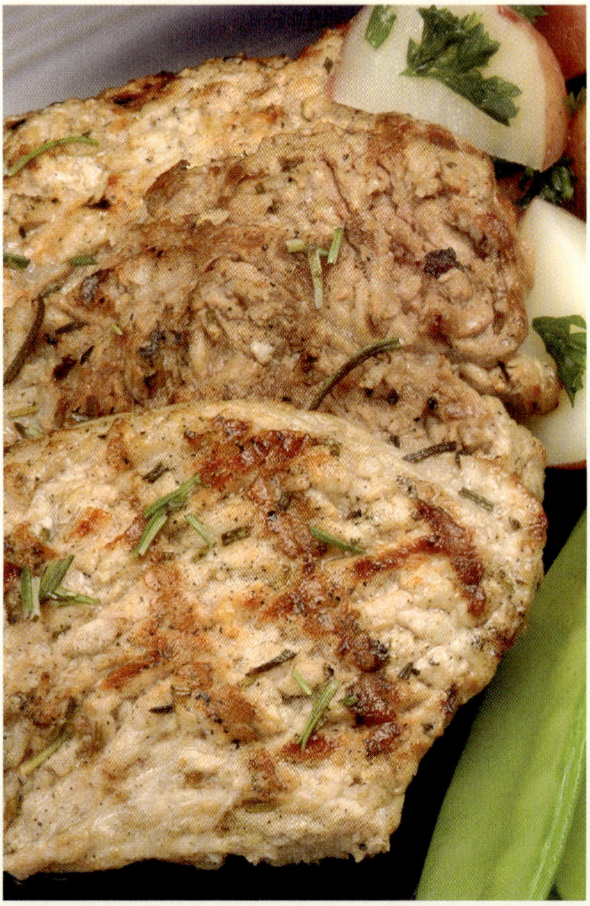

INDEX

Roasts

- 🍏 Asian Pork Noodle Soup, 31
- 🍏 Asian Pork and Rice Salad, 27
- Chinese-Style Barbecued Pork, 15
- Easy Caesar Pork Salad, 45
- German-Style Pork Roast, 19
- 🍏 Grilled Korean-Style Pork, 35
- Lexington Style Pork BBQ Sandwich, 47
- 🍏 Orange-Honey Marinated Pork Roast, 37
- 🍏 Parmesan Crusted Pork, 21
- 🍏 Pineapple Pork Steak, 17
- 🍏 Pork Chow Mein, 39
- 🍏 Pork and Hominy Soup, 25
- Pork and Pineapple Kabobs, 41
- Pork Roast with Peanut Sauce, 29
- 🍏 Pork Tenderloin with Cajun Rub, 43
- 🍏 Pork Vegetable Soup, 23
- 🍏 Slow-Cooked Cranberry Pork Tenderloin, 33

Chops

- Cranberry-Walnut Stuffed Pork Chops, 49
- 🍏 Curried Pork Stew, 73
- Fancy Pork Chop Casserole, 57
- 🍏 Grilled Pork Chops with Herb Rub, 59
- 🍏 Marinated Pork Cutlets, 69
- 🍏 Pork and Bean Salad, 55
- Pork Chops with Apricot Onion Marmalade, 51

Chops (Continued)

- 🍏 Pork Chops with Braised Red Cabbage, 63
- Pork Picatta, 53
- Pork and Wild Rice Casserole, 61
- Savory Pork Chop Pie, 65
- 🍏 Spicy Pork Lettuce Wraps, 71
- Southwest Enchilada Casserole, 67

Ribs

- Easy Oven Baked Ribs, 75
- Jerk Pork Ribs, 77
- 🍏 Oven Barbecued Country Style Ribs, 79
- Sticky Pork Ribs, 81

Ground

- Easy Pork Meatballs, 87
- Homemade Pasta Sauce, 83
- Lean Mean Chili & Beans, 89
- Pork-Filled Crescent Rolls, 91
- Pork-Spinach Meat Loaf, 93
- Southwestern Meat Loaf, 85

🍏 This symbol indicates a healthy recipe. See page 3, Good For You Choices, for details.

About Lowes Foods

With more than 100 stores throughout the Carolinas and Virginia, Lowes Foods is focused on offering fabulous, fresh foods and great groceries in a store format that is fast and easy to shop. We have a strong passion for quality and freshness because we know that even the best recipes are only as good as the ingredients that go into them.

Our customer-service focus has led us to develop innovative services such Lowes Foods To Go, our personal shopping service, and to offer customers the services of a Nutritionist.

We are committed to helping customers of all ages make healthier food choices throughout the year. To teach important lessons about nutrition and healthy lifestyles, we offer Be A Smart Shopper nutrition education field trips for children age 4 through 12. Recipes, meal plans and information about healthy eating are available on our website.

www.lowesfoods.com

For specific questions about nutrition and meal-planning,
please contact our nutritionist at
1-800-311-2117

good for you